1 8 6 6 - 1 9 9 1

125th

ANNIVERSARY

HEALTHY HEAD START

A Worry-free Guide to Feeding Young Children

Mary Abbott Hess, M.S., R.D.
Anne Elise Hunt
Barbara Motenko Stone

Marian Stevens, Illustrator

HENRY HOLT AND COMPANY ▪ NEW YORK

Copyright © 1990 by Mary Abbott Hess, M.S., R.D., Anne Elise Hunt,
Barbara Motenko Stone
Published by Henry Holt and Company, Inc.,
115 West 18th Street, New York, New York 10011.
Published in Canada by Fitzhenry & Whiteside Limited,
195 Allstate Parkway, Markham, Ontario L3R 4T8.

Library of Congress Cataloging-in-Publication Data
Hess, Mary Abbott.
A healthy head start : a worry-free guide to feeding young
children / by Mary Abbott Hess, Anne Elise Hunt, Barbara Motenko
Stone. — 1st ed.
p.   cm.
1. Children—Nutrition.   2. Cookery.   I. Hunt, Anne Elise.
II. Stone, Barbara Motenko.   III. Title.
RJ206.H43   1990   90-33523
641.5′622—dc20   CIP

ISBN 0-8050-1329-6
ISBN 0-8050-1838-7 (An Owl Book: pbk.)

Henry Holt books are available at special discounts
for bulk purchases for sales promotions, premiums,
fund-raising, or educational use. Special editions
or book excerpts can also be created to specification.
For details contact:
Special Sales Director, Henry Holt and Company, Inc.,
115 West 18th Street, New York, New York 10011

First published in hardcover by Henry Holt and Company,
Inc., in 1990.

FIRST OWL BOOK EDITION—1991

Book Design by Claire Naylon Vaccaro

Printed in the United States of America
Recognizing the importance of preserving the written word,
Henry Holt and Company, Inc., by policy, prints all of its
first editions on acid-free paper. ∞

10 9 8 7 6 5 4 3 2 1
10 9 8 7 6 5 4 3 2 1 (pbk.)

Grateful acknowledgment is made to Healthmere Press, Inc., for permission to
print a recipe adapted from More Recipes from Wooden Door, 1985.

Contents

Foreword

The authors of *A Healthy Head Start* asked me to write this foreword because of the two hats I wear, that of a pediatric endocrinology and metabolism specialist and that of a mother.

In my pediatric practice I see undernourished, overnourished, and well-nourished children with worried parents. The term "malnourished" can be applied to the overnourished, to the undernourished, and to those who are lacking in essential vitamins and minerals.

Malnutrition is not limited to the Third World or the poverty-stricken. Nutritional deficiency diseases occur even in the affluent suburbs of Chicago where I practice—not because of limited food resources but because of ignorance and misguided ideas about nutrition. Although malnutrition may have a medical basis, most malnutrition in this country is caused by poor dietary practices. I wish I had a nickel for every overweight child I treat whose parents have had to be told that inactivity or diet, not an underactive thyroid gland, is the source of the problem!

In recent years, I've seen an increasing number of children who look light enough to blow away in the wind. Their parents bring them to my office with cookies, juice, chips, and promises of ice cream if they are good for the doctor. These very concerned parents continuously ply the child with food—then wonder why the child stoically refuses to eat at meals.

Misguided family practices contribute to undesirable eating behaviors. The family's reactions to the way a child eats or doesn't eat can reinforce negative behavior and heighten rather than subdue tension around food. *A Healthy Head Start* offers an approach to the established problem eater.

Many eating problems can be averted, the book maintains, if parents and caregivers adopt a consistent approach that gives them responsibility for serving nutritious foods but lets the child decide what and how much he or she will eat. The authors support their program with sound nutrition information, practical suggestions for solving problems, and over two hundred recipes developed especially for young children.

Mann ist was Mann isst is a German phrase meaning "Man is what he eats." This may not be limited to the physical sense. Food enhances both the physical and the emotional quality of children's lives. *A Healthy Head Start* offers us, as parents, insight into how we might accomplish this with common sense, humor, and moderation.

Deborah V. Edidin, M.D.
Head, Division of Pediatric Endocrinology
Department of Pediatrics
Evanston Hospital, Evanston, Illinois

Assistant Professor, Pediatrics
Northwestern University Medical School

Introduction

"What shall I feed Elliott?" Lisa asked when her son began eating table food. After confidently giving him jars of fruit and vegetables and junior dinners, she wasn't sure what to do next. Lisa, like many of today's health-conscious parents, cares about both the quality and the quantity of food her child eats.

I'm Anne Hunt, one of the authors of *A Healthy Head Start*. Elliott is my grandson. Because I'm a health and nutrition writer, Lisa hoped I'd have the answer to her question. After all, I have written many articles and brochures on the subject.

My partner at Hess and Hunt, Inc., a nutrition communications firm near Chicago, is Mary Abbott Hess, a registered dietitian and health educator. She is a nationally known nutrition authority and is currently president of the American Dietetic Association, the largest group of nutrition professionals in the world.

Mary is often asked questions about feeding children: How much should a child eat? Do early eating practices prevent weight problems later in life? Can kids be taught to like foods that are good for them? How can you get a child to try new foods? What about fat and cholesterol and sugar and salt?

Shortly before we started work on this book, Mary had read reports about young children who failed to grow because of restrictive diets. Concerned parents, believing they were giving their children the best possible start, were applying adult standards and severely limiting fat and calories in their children's diets. The result was that some children didn't get what they needed to grow properly.

When Barbara Stone, who is an excellent cook and recipe developer, approached us about collaborating on *A Healthy Head Start*, both of us were interested and enthusiastic about the project. We liked the idea of combining advice on eating behavior and nutritional needs with recipes—the theory and practice of feeding kids.

Barbara had already created many of the recipes for the book, but she readily agreed to have Mary evaluate them. Mary not only knows her nutrition, but taught cooking and meal-planning courses for years and is author of the best-selling *The Art of Cooking for the Diabetic*. She knows a good recipe when she sees one! Mary and Barbara worked together, modifying some recipes and adding others.

My task was to write the chapters that precede the recipes. To make sure that the book didn't dwell too much on theory and not enough on practice, I interviewed parents and included "real-life" feeding experiences in the text. We want to give practical advice, not make parents feel guilty. Mary, with her technical background in nutrition (she was a nutrition professor at Mundelein College in Chicago), developed the charts and lists and revised the copy.

When we were done, we sent the manuscript to experts on pediatric nutrition and child development. Their comments and suggestions are included in this book. We thank them for their valuable input:

Harriet Holt Cloud, M.S., R.D.
Director, Nutrition Division
Sparks Center for Development and Learning Disorders
University of Alabama, Birmingham

Susan Calvert Finn, Ph.D., R.D.
Director, Nutrition Services
Ross Laboratories
Columbus, Ohio

Ellyn Satter, M.S., M.S.S.W., R.D.
Therapist
Family Therapy Center
Madison, Wisconsin
Author of *How to Get Your Kid to Eat . . . but Not Too Much* and
    Child of Mine: Feeding with Love and Good Sense

Alice E. Smith, M.S., R.D.
Director of Clinical Dietetics
Children's Memorial Hospital
Chicago, Illinois

·BUDDING·
TASTERS

All parents want their children to be "good eaters"—to eat their vegetables, drink their milk, and stay within an acceptable weight range. Are "good eaters" born or made?

Psychotherapist and eating/feeding specialist Ellyn Satter writes about "the feeding relationship." In a supportive relationship, the parent respects and responds to the child's signals about when, what, how much, and at what pace food is eaten. The child then develops positive attitudes about him- or herself and the world—"Hey, they love me and think I'm important!" "Good eaters," then, are both born (with the ability to self-regulate eating behavior) and made (by parents who provide a variety of healthful foods within a structure that responds to their child's feeding cues).

The wise parent responds to the challenges and limitations of each child's physical and emotional development and doesn't underestimate the power of social and cultural influences on eating habits. A child quickly learns to eat food the way the family commonly prepares it, and finds that he or she can get attention or approval by accepting or rejecting certain foods.

Physical Development and Eating Behavior

Comfort is an often overlooked factor that influences eating. One- and two-year-olds need firm support for their body and legs when they eat. They also need a safe, confined place because they have a short attention span, are easily distracted, and are likely to stand up in the chair. Don't be too quick to give up the high chair!

A booster chair is acceptable if the child's legs aren't left dangling. Children like a small table and chair for snacks or meals when they aren't eating with the family.

Most children can feed themselves without help by fifteen months—if they are allowed to do so. When children begin to eat independently, they can manage only a few bites at the start of the meal when they are hungriest and most interested. Then the parent or caregiver should step in to feed the remainder of the meal. When a child spends ten minutes feeding him- or herself, it's time to turn almost all eating responsibility over to the child.

The presence of teeth does not necessarily mean that a child has mastered the art of chewing and swallowing. Some children will swallow food almost whole; others will gum it and then hold it in their cheeks like a chipmunk.

Not long ago a dentist who had referred patients to Hess and Hunt, Inc., for nutrition counseling called seeking advice about his daughter's eating. "My wife and I are worried about Samantha. She's fifteen months old and won't eat anything," he told us. The parents were invited to bring Samantha and discuss the problem over lunch in the Hess and Hunt test kitchen.

The family arrived with jars of junior baby food for Samantha, and the battle began! Samantha neither wanted to feed herself nor to be fed. Mary Abbott Hess casually reached across the table and offered the child a piece of her pita bread sandwich. To the amazement of her parents, Samantha gobbled it down and held out her hand for more. She sampled Mary's thinly sliced cucumbers and tomatoes before she'd had enough and was ready to explore other areas of the office.

The concerned parents explained that they had tried giving Samantha table food several times before, but when she refused it or ate very little, they assumed she preferred the soft-textured junior foods. Worried about her getting enough to eat, they had gone back to food they could spoon into her mouth.

Some children do prefer soft foods that are easy to chew. Parents must guard against encouraging them to become lazy eaters by providing a variety of foods with different textures. Samantha, however, was bored with junior foods and wanted *more* texture. She wanted to eat what she saw others eating. She didn't express this in a way her parents could understand. Other children point or reach for foods they want—she simply refused to eat. When Samantha had more control over her food, she was more interested in eating, and the problem was quickly resolved.

Sense-sational Food

Much of what we know about sensory development was discovered during attempts in the seventies and eighties to find bad-tasting or bad-smelling substances that would keep children from eating lead-based paint and poisonous household products.

Researchers found that while a newborn can detect its own mother by smell, the olfactory senses linked to food do not develop fully until a child is four or five years old. A three-year-old, for example, cannot taste vanilla, which is not detected even by adults unless it is also smelled. And it is the bright red color and sweetness of cherry-flavored foods, not the distinctive smell, that appeals to toddlers.

During the early years, when a child's senses are still immature, the shape, color, and arrangement of food plays a major role in food acceptance. A few bright green, fresh or thawed frozen peas, a slice of avocado, or a spoonful of chopped red tomato can entice a reticent diner to venture a taste—and maybe even swallow some of it. Anne's middle daughter, Jennifer, loved parsley ("garni," she called it) when she was a little girl. She wanted it on her plate for breakfast, lunch, and dinner.

Children prefer foods that, like Goldilocks's porridge, are "not too hot, not too cold, but ju-u-u-ust right!" Adult gourmets confirm their preferences. Also, some dry foods don't taste good to kids. Because they have less saliva than older eaters, kids prefer foods "juicy" or moistened with a little sauce or gravy.

In his book *On Food and Cooking*, Harold McGee says, "Our palate will be sharper, more attentive to nuance if it is entertained, kept off guard, given something new every few bites. Contrast and variety are biologically certifiable culinary principles."

Sensory Skill-Building

Foods offer wonderful opportunities to enrich sensory skills. Here are several activities that are fun and will increase your child's awareness of the color, smell, texture, and flavor of foods.

Color Me Delicious!

At the grocery store or farmers' market, pick out fruits and vegetables by color. Have children arrange foods by color on a plate or platter.

Smelly Food

A four- or five-year-old child can detect the distinctive smell of fresh fruit: pineapple, oranges, strawberries. Try herbs and spices: cinnamon, cloves, garlic. Make a recipe using a favorite smelly food, such as garlicky Aioli Sauce (see page 226), fragrant Ring Around the Mango (see page 285), or Lamb Choplets (see page 182) that smell like rosemary.

Snap, Crackle, Pop

Learning to appreciate the texture of a food helps children become discriminating in their taste preferences. Ask your young taster to describe how these foods feel in his or her mouth: sugar snap peas, avocado, raw or crisp-cooked cauliflower, ripe pear, whole-grain bread, string cheese, jicama, and tofu.

Primary Taste Test

Taste buds are sensitive to four primary stimuli. Introduce your young sensory evaluator to the basic food flavors. You may be surprised by some of the reactions!

Sour: lemon, rhubarb, plain yogurt, dill pickle
Bitter: radish, cooked turnip greens, watercress
Sweet: ripe pineapple, mango, sweet potato
Salty: pretzels, salted nuts, some canned soups

Your role as a parent is to be sensitive to your child's individual likes and dislikes while providing opportunities to enrich sensory skills and expand food experiences.

If you prepare a special food, it's only natural that you want your whole family to enjoy it. But you should not *make* your child eat specific foods—that's his or her choice and responsibility.

The best way to encourage your child to try a food is to set an example. Evidence suggests that a child's—like a parent's or a peer's—liking for a food is a critical sociocultural influence in his or her food choices and has a lasting impact on attitudes about food throughout life. Cultural and social eating habits have more influence than individual taste preferences. Why else would toddlers in Mexico eat hot chilies and East Indian preschoolers down their curries?

TASTE BUD TRAINING

- Present new foods at the beginning of a meal when your child is most hungry.

- Serve small portions of new foods. If the food is not accepted, take it away without fuss and present it again a few days later. It sometimes takes many exposures for the food to become familiar enough for your child to venture a bite.

- Don't reward children for "trying just a bite." Preschoolers are less likely to eat a new food again if they are rewarded than if they are just exposed to the food and allowed to try it.

- Make food look beautiful and appetizing.

- Introduce a variety of seasonings but respect individual taste preferences.

- Add a little juice or sauce to dry foods because children prefer moist textures.

- Serve foods warm, at room temperature, or chilled, rather than very hot or icy cold.

- Set an example. Children raised during the time of the Holy Roman Empire learned to love garum, a sauce made of salted fermented fish intestines. Your son or daughter can come to appreciate yogurt dressing, pesto sauce, and even liver!

·TIME TO EAT!·

There's a big difference between appetite and hunger. Appetite is an *externally induced* desire for food—the way you respond when you pass a Mrs. Field's cookie store, smell bread baking, or view a television ad showing a frosty cold drink.

Hunger is the body's *internal*, stomach-grumbling and brain-directed physiologic need for food. The hunger mechanism often becomes distorted during early childhood because adults insist that kids eat when they aren't hungry; because kids are not allowed to eat when they *are* hungry; and because kids are given food when they need something else, like attention or a nap.

Regular Mealtimes

If you schedule meals and snacks at least one and a half to two hours apart during the day, your child will come to the table hungry and ready to eat. Don't be surprised if, after you shop through your child's regular mealtime, you have a cranky, hungry child on your hands. And don't expect a youngster who's sampled the hors d'oeuvres to be enthusiastic about meat loaf and squash half an hour later.

With today's busy and sometimes unpredictable schedules, it's best to be flexible about this advice. If you pick up your kids after work and know it will be at least an hour before you can get dinner on the table, offer a piece of fruit or crackers to tide them over.

Research shows that young children who are allowed to eat until their hunger is satisfied, regardless of how little or how much food that may mean, are less likely to become obese or develop eating problems when they are older. If you insist that food be eaten, you can interfere with your child's internal hunger control and may promote overeating. If you withhold food when your child wants more, he or she may overeat even when not really hungry, fearing there may not be enough the next time.

Because hunger varies from day to day, and even from meal to meal, it is difficult to predict when a child will eat only bites and when the same child will want two full portions of the very same food. These inconsistencies are frustrating to the person who prepares and serves the food. Some people take it as personal rejection when a young child refuses to eat. This can create a power and control battle that leads to forcing, bribing, or other negative feeding behaviors.

Changing Needs

Eating behavior is influenced by "development," the ability to function with certain skills, such as handling a spoon and feeding oneself. Hunger is also influenced by growth. "Growth" is the addition of tissue, thus resulting in an increase in physical size. The faster a child grows, the greater the need for food. Remember feeding your newborn every three or four hours? That baby was growing every minute! By the end of the first year, most babies' weights are about triple what they were at birth, and height typically increases by 50 percent.

The sudden change in the eating habits of toddlers worries parents. They think their child will surely starve because he or she refuses to eat. Remember, your child's body knows best. During the second year, weight gain is only one-third or one-half pound a month, and it doesn't take as much energy to sustain dramatically slower growth. Toddlers will begin to look taller and slimmer as they begin to use body stores of baby fat to supplement calorie intake. Children will eat as much as they need if adequate food is offered.

Usually, by age four, development enters an easier stage. Four- and five-year-olds enjoy eating more. They are better at chewing and swallowing, are neater eaters, and like eating with the rest of the family and other children. Until age nine or ten, growth proceeds at a slow but constant rate. Eating is seldom as important or demanding as other interests.

The hunger mechanism is sensitive to activity levels. When there is little activity, the body gets the message that it should prepare for hibernation or a famine. Hunger increases, calling for more calories to build up reserves. Increasing activity, on the other hand, causes the release of adrenaline and other hormones that can decrease hunger. Exercise burns calories not only during activity but afterward as well. Exercise retards excessive weight gain and builds aerobic strength during the growing years. Increasing activity is good for almost all children and adults. In addition to promoting fitness and muscle strength, it encourages the development of strong bones and burns excess calories.

BOOSTER CHAIR GUIDELINES

- Avoid using food to pacify or reward behavior.

- Feed your child at regular intervals to allow hunger to develop for a meal or snack.

- Slow down! It takes about twenty minutes for the brain to get the signal that the body has been fed. Slow eaters are less likely to overeat than fast eaters.

- Don't provide a nonstop supply of fluids, such as juice and milk, which curtail hunger.

- Give your child more food if he or she wants it.

- Remove food as soon as there are signs that your child is no longer hungry.

- Increase activity.

Enough to Eat

There is only one way to tell if your child is getting enough to eat: Is he or she growing? Generally a parent can't evaluate whether or not a child is growing normally. Doctors measure children's growth and plot the figures on a growth chart that shows development over time. If the relationship of height to weight is not balanced, or the child is above the ninetieth percentile of weight and height for his or her age, the doctor will look for a cause. If there are no health, nutrition, or emotional problems, the child is probably genetically predetermined to be as he or she is. A child's height often correlates with parents' height.

In the 1970s a lot was written about the "fat-cell theory." Based on original research with animals, this theory suggested that young children who were obese developed more fat cells than normal-weight children. These individuals, according to the theory, were predestined to become fat adults. From their studies, researchers hypothesized that the total number of fat cells is determined by nutritional factors soon after birth and that fat-cell size is regulated by nutrition later in life.

Subsequent studies have shown that cell numbers can increase during adult years if there is prolonged excessive overeating or can decrease if a person loses a great deal of weight, and keeps it off, for a time.

Research continues on the fat-cell theory. One thing seems clear: Those who have larger fat cells are at greater risk of heart disease, high blood pressure, and many other medical problems than those who have more fat cells. Thus it makes sense to avoid continual overeating at any age. Exercise, which we know influences fat-cell metabolism, also helps to limit fat-cell development.

If your child is chubby, you may be having a very hard time accepting it. Will your friends think you allow him or her to overeat? Will he or she grow up to be an obese adult?

"I didn't worry about my son," one mother told us, "but I had this horror of my daughter being a fat teenager." Beginning in infancy and continuing throughout their lives, females have more body fat than males—and often mothers who nag them about it.

Studies show little correlation between childhood and adult obesity until girls are nine years old. In fact, the rapid weight gain of boys between two and six years is more predictive of long-term weight problems. Any boy *or* girl who experiences rapid weight gain or loss should receive prompt medical evaluation.

Parents who are anxious or ambivalent about their own eating, particularly chronic dieters, are often very concerned about preventing their children from becoming overweight. They are more likely to restrain the child's eating by withholding food, limiting time to eat, or limiting the amount of food given. Unfortunately, this can set up a tendency in the child to overeat in response to stress that can promote weight-control problems later in life.

Young children should not be put on a reducing diet, even if they are overweight. Dieting can interfere with bone, muscle, and brain development. If your child is overweight, have a registered dietitian evaluate the calories he or she is eating. The dietitian will work with you to develop ways to increase activity and may suggest lower-calorie foods that will provide adequate nutrients. The goal is to slow down further weight gain until height catches up to the weight on the growth chart.

During the adjustment period, continue to offer a variety of healthful foods and allow your child to regulate the amount eaten. Don't withhold food or pressure a child to eat less. Often this pressure backfires, causing intensified interest in food and eating and a fear of being hungry, which only promotes overeating and more weight gain. Sometimes a child gets extra attention by overeating, and the attention reinforces that behavior. The solution to the problem may be deemphasizing eating and providing extra love and attention at other times and during other activities.

Children need a lot of love—whether they are thin, normal, or overweight. Helping your child feel secure is important. Children with weight "problems" present a special parenting challenge. If *you* can't accept your child for how he or she is, you can undermine your child's self-esteem and emotional development.

Talk to a family counselor. An overweight youngster is often a family problem. It is the parents who control where, when, and what a child eats. Mealtimes and eating take place in a family setting. Without even realizing it, parents may promote their child's weight problem. When weight changes, the family dynamics and focus may shift. Changes in family dynamics may be difficult for some family members to accept.

Ellyn Satter, who counsels overweight children and their parents, cautions against unrealistic expectations. "Success in terms of weight loss may be limited," she says, "but success in terms of enhancing emotional well-being, nutritional status, and physical capability may be considerable."

Brain Food

The brain has critical periods of anatomical, physiological, bio-chemical, and psychological growth and development. These critical periods begin shortly after conception and continue through the first three years of life. By eighteen months, a human has all the brain cells that he or she will ever have. But these cells continue to grow in size and develop in structure and capability. The weight of the brain increases until about age six, reflecting an increase in the size of cells.

As a way of tracking brain growth, the doctor measures a child's head circumference. During the first year, the baby's brain size increases about four and three-quarters inches. During the second year, head circumference increases only about three-quarters of an inch. By the end of the first year the brain reaches two-thirds of its adult size and at the end of the second year, about four-fifths.

Adequate calories and protein are important during all stages of brain development. Severe nutritional deprivation before eighteen months has been shown to slow the rate of cell division and thus permanently reduce the total number of brain cells. A child on a low-fat diet is deprived of essential fatty acids that contribute to the brain's gray matter. "A low-fat diet during the first two years of life could have long-term detrimental effects on a child's intelligence," cautions Chicago pediatrician Howard M. Rice, M.D.

After eighteen months, and throughout the preschool years, the quality of the diet, primarily protein and calories, can influence the development and size of brain cells. Even if a child doesn't eat a great deal, there is no cause for concern about brain growth, as long as some food is eaten.

Although you may have heard otherwise, no single foods have the power to increase intelligence or improve mental capacity. Diets that promote eating specific foods at particular times of day to increase intelligence make good table conversation but are not supported by solid scientific evidence.

While studies have shown that iron levels in the blood can affect cognitive development, nutrition does not have a major influence on intellectual development. Intelligence is related to heredity and the availability of an environment that stimulates intellectual and educational development. One study, conducted by Dr. Myron Winick, revealed that previously malnourished Korean children who were adopted into middle-class American homes achieved completely normal IQs.

It is true, however, that children who are severely malnourished have more emotional and behavioral problems than well-nourished children. Concurrent with severe malnourishment, these children often experience minimal stimulation, receive little attention, have little space to explore, and so on. Some studies report more immature behavior, more clumsiness, and less sociability in previously malnourished children. Providing good food is only one part of meeting developmental needs. Fortunately, the parents and caregivers who read this book are likely to provide a stimulating environment and many opportunities for optimal physical, social, and emotional development.

·I'LL COOK,·
YOU EAT

Feeding a preschooler is a creative and educational experience, as well as an act of providing physical nourishment. For young children, eating is both a means of self-expression and a way to satisfy hunger. The challenge to parents is to encourage individualism within a framework that provides healthful foods and positive eating habits. "I won't let you do whatever you please, but I can provide freedom of choice within safe and acceptable limits" is the kind of attitude that will yield positive results. By providing consistent, age-appropriate limits, you can encourage self-expression without allowing your child to become obnoxious.

Dietitian and therapist Ellyn Satter shares these facts about children's eating:

- Children will eat.
- They are capable of regulating their food intake.
- They generally react negatively to new foods but will usually accept them with time and experience.
- Parents can either support or disrupt children's food acceptance and food regulation.

In her excellent book *How to Get Your Kid to Eat . . . but Not Too Much* (Bull Publishing Company, 1987), Satter gives the golden rule of feeding to parents: "Parents are responsible for what is presented to eat and the manner in which it is presented. Children are responsible for how much and even whether they eat."

Easier said than done! you may be thinking. We know how tempting it is to urge "Just three more bites" or "Eat it for Mommy." But, Satter assures, you'll have fewer problems and less finicky eating if you let children take responsibility for their eating.

The Temperamental Gourmet

From eighteen months to three years of age, most children go through a stage that concerns and frustrates parents. Developmentally, this is a time for asserting independence. "No 'matoes!" Anne Hunt's daughter Mary announced definitively when she was a toddler. At age twenty-two she still picks the 'matoes out of a salad. In young children, meat and potatoes that are eagerly devoured on Monday may be totally unacceptable a week later. The milk drinker wants juice; the juice lover wants milk. Just put the food on the table, including one or two items that your child usually eats, along with a favorite food, such as bread.

Demanding the same food day after day is a common enough occurrence among youngsters to have earned a label—"food jag." Experts say that the best way to deal with food jags is to treat them matter-of-factly. Food jags are less likely to become a problem if an adult remains in control of the menu. But children, like adults, have foods they particularly enjoy. If the child wants the same food at every meal, you may give it to him or her but continue to offer a choice. Try offering the food as a regular snack but not as part of the dinner menu. When the child feels secure that the demand for a particular food will be met, he or she is less likely to be preoccupied with it. Parents need to be concerned only if there are real nutritional risks, which might occur if a food jag severely limits food intake or lasts more than several weeks. Consult a physician if you are in doubt.

Marketing experts know the value of presenting options when they want to make a sale. "Do you want Plan A or Plan B?" "No" is not an option. This tactic works well in parenting, too. "Do you want to wear the red shirt or the blue shirt?" "Would you like the sauce on top of or next to your spaghetti?" "Shall we buy shell macaroni or the bows?" Just don't ask, "What would you like to eat?" You may be the chief cook and bottle washer, but you needn't be a short-order cook or offer a full menu of food choices!

The Curious Gourmet

Curiosity may be the mother of invention, but to many mothers, the curiosity of their offspring requires lots of patience and understanding. A toddler will pull apart a sandwich, pour milk into the applesauce, or squeeze the squash between all ten fingers. Food goes in and out of the mouth, onto the floor, and on top of the head. Put newspaper or a vinyl-coated tablecloth or pad under the child's chair, present the food invitingly, and offer no comments about the manner in which the food is consumed (or not consumed). Eat or sit with the child or at least be in the room, and be sociable. Don't feel that mealtime requires constant entertainment. In fact, some children are so easily distracted that it's better to maintain a calm atmosphere. If your child becomes excited during family meals, let him or her start eating before others come to the table.

Now comes the hardest part of this scenario: no food until the next snack or meal. This rule holds true for older preschoolers as well, who should be told before they are excused from the table that there will be no eating until the next meal. When your children realize that the only time there is food is at regular meal and snack times, they will eat at meals.

The positive side of a child's curiosity is that he or she may be quite willing to try a variety of foods. Introduce new foods when your child is most hungry and not tired or excited. Give only a small portion and show your acceptance of the food by eating it, too. Don't make a big thing of either rejection or acceptance.

By nature, children are neophobic—afraid to try something new. You may have to present a new food ten or more times before your cautious gourmet gets up enough courage to put it into his or her mouth. Don't flinch if it goes into and out of the mouth several times before it actually gets eaten. Mary Abbott Hess remembers when, as a child, she was told she couldn't leave the table until she ate her peas. She sat at the table long after the family meal. To this day, she hates peas.

Offer "who can resist" arrangements of colorful foods of interesting shapes and sizes, such as Speared Poultry (see page 189) with Spinach Fingers (see page 139) and cherry tomato quarters, for instance. Kids especially like bite-size pieces—carrot coins, baby squash, and melon balls.

A bright place mat, plate, or fork with a colored handle may appeal to your toddler's waning interest at mealtime. On the other hand, a two-year-old may demand "my plate, my cup, and my fork." That's okay. We all like special things around us and the feeling of security they bring.

Helping Hands

By the time youngsters are two, they want to do everything themselves. Now that they have good control of finger muscles, they can help themselves from a serving bowl and spread margarine on the bread. They can take an active part in the selection and preparation of food. A three-year-old can help set the table and maybe even help clean up afterward. Praise every effort. Resist the impulse to rearrange to make it neater. Washing unbreakable lunch or snack dishes in a pan of soapy water makes a fine summer backyard activity.

Elicit the help of your four- or five-year-old in putting away the clean silverware or putting napkins on the table. These activities are the first steps in teaching your children basic "survival skills" that will be with them throughout life. Enjoy your preschooler's eagerness to help. You won't get this kind of response from a ten- or twelve-year-old!

Setting an Example

Family meals are an essential part of a child's education. Not only do children learn about food and eating behavior, but they learn family traditions, history, and positions on social issues.

Think back to the dinner table of your childhood. Do you remember where everyone sat? Did you have rituals associated with meals? Pass along some of the good memories to your children.

KINDERKITCHEN

The recipes in this book are not meant for children to do on their own, but they'll enjoy helping you . . .

- Add vegetables to soup.

- Wash spinach.

- Spoon sandwich mixtures onto bagels or bread.

- Cut cheese shapes with cookie cutters.

- Add liquid to and mix muffin batter.

- Shuck fresh corn.

- Separate cauliflower and broccoli flowerets.

- Mix the salad (in a very large bowl).

- Cut soft vegetables and fruit with a table knife.

- Scrub potatoes.

- Knead dough.

- Season chicken and fish.

- Sprinkle cheese on tacos and tarts.

Anne's one-year-old granddaughter, Erin, folds her hands for grace before meals and claps when her brother Elliott announces "Now eat!" after the blessing.

Establish your own family traditions, too—Wednesday is pasta day; Saturday is Dad's day to fix breakfast; Sunday is midday special dinner.

When we eat together, family members develop a sense of belonging and sharing. As we talk about what we've done during the day and what our plans are for the future, we learn about one another. Communication relieves stress and improves self-image.

Keep mealtime conversation light. This is not the time to discuss the household budget, irritating relatives, or office politics. Find ways to include younger diners in the conversation.

Regardless of the old adage, it is not normal for children to be seen but not heard at the dinner table. But do teach your child that there are limits, and that he or she is expected to control his or her behavior. These limits should be appropriate for the child's age. The attention span of a five-year-old is only fifteen minutes!

Children quickly learn how to get attention when they want it: biting a playmate, having a tantrum in the supermarket—or turning their cereal bowl upside down. If a parent responds appropriately, but without getting emotionally hooked, the behavior is less likely to be repeated.

If socially unacceptable behavior does occur, take the child away from the table for a private chat. Make it clear that if things don't improve, eating alone before the rest of the family is the consequence. Be realistic in your expectations, and watch for signs that your young diner is through eating, then let him or her leave the table and go play or watch television until others finish eating.

Child development experts tell us that excessive mealtime rules can lead to eating problems later in life. Keep instructions about mealtime manners to a minimum. But do teach basic table manners. Too many young people today think a sit-down meal means putting carry-out or quick-fix microwaved food on a plate instead of eating it right out of the carton! They're at a loss when confronted by a table setting of multiple knives, forks, and spoons. Practice at home what you expect when you take your child out to a restaurant or to a friend's home for dinner.

If children make negative comments about the food, cut them off with "Try the applesauce—you may like it better," then change the subject. Be positive about food. Talk about which foods each of you likes best, about the fresh corn or tomatoes from the garden. Let your enthusiasm about the meal rub off on your youngster.

Yet another reason to encourage good table talk is that research shows that children (and presumably their parents, too) who talk more at meals are less likely to overeat than those who don't take time in between bites to chat. (We all know you shouldn't talk with your mouth full!)

·MENU FOR·
GOOD NUTRITION

W e've said a great deal about a child's ability to respond to innate hunger and satiety. What a child will not do is instinctively choose a well-balanced diet. In the 1920s a researcher offered a number of young children a selection of foods and, based on their choices, concluded that they preferred healthful foods. What was not remembered in the years that followed was that the children were offered *only* nutritious foods, so no "poor" choices were available. Our advice to you is to reproduce the experiment: Offer only healthful foods!

The RDAs—Recommended Dietary Allowances—list protein, calories, eleven vitamins, and seven minerals that healthy infants, children, and adults need each day. The recommendations are measured in grams, micrograms, milligrams, and several equivalents. This makes nutrition sound very complicated. It also can worry parents who realize that their children eat very small amounts of food: Are they getting all the nutrients they need?

Nutrition is food, not numbers. If your family eats a variety of healthful foods, you don't have to worry about the numbers.

Parents who entrust their children to baby-sitters or day-care providers have to balance the children's eating with other aspects of physical well-being and with social, intellectual, and emotional growth.

If someone comes to care for your child at your home, you can set out the ground rules and provide the foods you want served. If you are using a private sitter, you have every right to expect your basic meal plan to be followed. Discuss your attitudes and feeding practices with the sitter. You might ask the sitter to read this book.

It's harder when you take your child to a home-care situation or day-care center, where there are other children. In some situations, you can send along food for snacks and lunches, but even then, your child will be influenced by what the other children are eating. If food is provided, you have little control.

Many licensed centers and day-care homes follow planning guidelines to meet the RDAs for children. Be sure to evaluate the types of food served when you select day care. Ask what is served and observe portion sizes and feeding practices. Do the other children eat well? Is the environment pleasant? Is the food prepared in a clean kitchen? Are the meals and snacks served acceptable to you? Are the children allowed to pick and choose from foods that are offered? Can they eat as much or as little as they like?

If the answer to any of these questions is no, then look elsewhere for day care. You are unlikely to be satisfied and the center is unlikely to change.

The Essentials

Humans need to eat six substances to sustain life: vitamins, minerals, protein, carbohydrate, fat, and water. These nutrients must be supplied from outside the body. While supplements in pill form contain some of them, food is still their best source. After all, food, not supplements, is what humans have lived on for thousands of years. Scientists think there are some nutrients, as yet undiscovered, that are in food but not included in supplements. In addition, nutrients are absorbed in combinations that occur naturally in foods. And food contains acids/bases, proteins, and other substances that promote nutrient absorption and use. Last, the concentrations of nutrients in a variety of foods are adequate to meet human needs; high-strength supplements, on the other hand, may oversupply to dangerous levels, especially if given to children.

Although everyone can eat the same foods, portion sizes will vary for different family members. Children need snacks to meet nutrient and caloric needs because they usually eat small amounts at meals.

Most adults who eat full portions don't need snacks to meet daily needs. If you are pregnant or breast-feeding and have either a small capacity or increased needs, try adopting the diet of a small child— three healthful meals and several healthful snacks.

Most preschoolers who eat a variety of healthful foods get the essential nutrients they need to grow, even if they are picky eaters. If your child has special needs or intolerances to many foods that restrict nutrient intake, the doctor may prescribe a supplement of particular nutrients. Follow the doctor's orders, but under no circumstances should you give your child nonprescribed, self-selected supplements, especially supplements meant for adults. Excessive amounts of vitamins and minerals can create a nutritional imbalance or a dangerous toxic reaction.

The Food Group Plan

The food group plan is a simple way to plan meals for your family. By including several foods from each group every day, you can be sure that you are offering a balanced diet. You need not be concerned about counting individual grams or milligrams of specific nutrients.

Our food groups are a simple system that groups together foods that supply similar, but not identical, nutrients. Food groups are a generic way to organize similar foods, and there are a variety of food group plans in different publications. For example, all foods on our fruit group list contain carbohydrate, vitamins, and minerals. The list is then further divided to show which fruits are richest in vitamin A and vitamin C. Some items on the list, such as dried fruits and blueberries, are also rich in fiber, while others, such as fruit juice, have virtually no fiber.

By serving a variety of foods from the fruit group list, you offer all the key nutrients in that group.

When planning children's diets, quality and variety are more important than quantity. On the following pages we list a recommended number of servings (and portion sizes) to give you an idea of what to offer, but there are wide variations from child to child, meal to meal, and day to day. Serve the suggested child-size portion and let your young eater ask for more, if he or she wants it. The bottom line is the growth chart kept by your doctor.

In this book, we have divided foods in each group into "Best Choices" and "Other Choices." The recipes use many ingredients that are on the "Best Choices" food lists. We're not saying that other foods are "bad"—there's room for many foods in a varied, balanced meal plan. The "Best Choices" foods have a better nutritional profile than "Other Choices" foods—more vitamins and minerals and often less fat, salt, or sweetening. Buy mostly "Best Choices" foods and serve them for meals and snacks. Your whole family, as well as your preschool child, will benefit.

Foods to Offer Every Day

Serve the recommended number of servings from *each* of the food groups every day.

Milk and Dairy Group

Recommended servings and typical serving sizes:

Ages 1 to 3: Two to three servings daily
One serving = 1/2 cup to 3/4 cup milk
= 1/2 cup to 3/4 cup yogurt
= 1 ounce (1 slice) hard cheese
= 1/4 cup cottage cheese, pudding, ice milk, or ice cream

Ages 4 to 5: Two to three servings daily
One serving = 3/4 cup milk
= 3/4 cup yogurt
= 1 1/2 ounces hard cheese
= 1/2 cup cottage cheese, pudding, ice milk, or ice cream

BEST MILK/DAIRY CHOICES

Whole milk (before age 2)
Low-fat milk (after age 2)

Buttermilk
Plain yogurt (low-fat after age 2)
Cheeses (except very-high-fat cheese, such as Brie)
Cottage cheese
Evaporated milk
Evaporated skim milk
Kefir
Ricotta cheese

OTHER MILK/DAIRY CHOICES

Chocolate milk
Pudding, custard
Fruited yogurt
Sweetened fruited yogurt
Ice cream
Ice milk
Frozen yogurt
Cream soups
Very-high-fat cheeses
Milkshakes

WHAT YOU MAY NOT KNOW:

• Offer milk as a beverage at least twice a day. Milk is rich in protein, calcium, and vitamins A and D. While ice cream and milkshakes are fine occasionally, they should not be used as a milk replacement as they are much higher in fat and sugar and far lower in the protein, vitamins, and minerals your child needs. Two to three glasses of milk provide these nutrients. There is no nutritional benefit to drinking more milk. Don't let your child fill up on milk or there won't be room for foods from other food groups.

• Skim milk is seldom recommended for preschoolers. Give one- to two-year-olds whole milk, then switch them to 2 percent milk or 1 percent milk as advised by the doctor.

• Without milk, it's hard for a child to get the recommended 800 milligrams of calcium each day. A combination of other calcium-containing foods typically contributes a total of only 300 milligrams a day. One eight-ounce glass of milk has 280 milligrams of calcium!

• If milk must be avoided because of medically proven allergy or intolerance, a registered dietitian can suggest ways to obtain adequate calcium.

• Don't replace milk with juice! Juice has carbohydrate and some vitamins and minerals, but young children need the calcium and protein in milk.

• Cottage cheese, while an excellent low-fat dairy product, has far less calcium than a child-size portion of milk, yogurt, or hard cheese.

• Cream cheese is not included in this food group because it contains primarily fat and not the protein-containing solids that are in most other cheeses. Cream cheese is on the fats and oils list.

Fruit Group

Recommended servings and typical serving sizes:

Ages 1 to 3: Two or more servings daily. Include one vitamin C–rich fruit (or vegetable) daily; plus 3 tablespoons vitamin A–rich fruit (or vegetable) every other day.
  One serving = ½ small whole fruit (such as apple or banana)
            = ¼ cup canned or cooked fruit
            = ½ cup juice
            = ½ cup grapes or melon balls
            = 2 tablespoons dried fruit

Ages 4 to 5: Two or more servings daily. Include one vitamin C–rich fruit (or vegetable) daily; plus 4 tablespoons vitamin A–rich fruit (or vegetable) every other day.
  One serving = ½ to 1 whole small fruit (such as apple or banana)
            = ⅓ cup canned or cooked fruit
            = ½ cup juice
            = ½ cup grapes or melon balls
            = 2 tablespoons dried fruit

BEST FRUIT CHOICES

VITAMIN C—RICH

Cantaloupe
Gooseberries
Grapefruit
Guava
Frozen fortified
   fruit juice bar
Honeydew melon
Lemon
Kiwifruit
Mandarin orange
Mango
Nectarine
Orange
Papaya
Strawberries
Tangerine

VITAMIN A—RICH

Apricot
Cantaloupe
Guava
Mango
Nectarine
Papaya
Persimmon
Plantain
Plum (canned)
Prunes
Watermelon

SECOND-BEST FRUIT CHOICES

(contain less vitamin A and C)

Apple
Applesauce
Avocado
Banana
Blackberries
Blueberries
Casaba melon
Cherries
Currants
Dates

Figs
Fruit cocktail
Grapes
Peach
Pear
Pineapple
Pomegranate
Plum (fresh)
Raisins
Raspberries
Rhubarb

BEST FRUIT-JUICE CHOICES

VITAMIN C–RICH

Blended citrus juice
Cranapple juice (fortified
  with vitamin C)
Cranberry cocktail
Grape juice (fortified
  with vitamin C)
Grapefruit juice
Orange juice
Tangerine juice

VITAMIN A–RICH

Apricot nectar
Peach nectar
Papaya nectar

SECOND-BEST FRUIT-JUICE CHOICES

Apple juice
Cider
Fruit drinks
Fruit punch
Mixed juice
Pear nectar
Pineapple juice
Prune juice (rich in iron)

OTHER FRUIT AND FRUIT-JUICE CHOICES

(containing more sugar and/or fat)

Fruit pies, cobblers, tarts
Fruit spreads, jams
Fortified fruit drinks
Lemonade

WHAT YOU MAY NOT KNOW:

• Some fruits, especially dried fruits, berries, and solid fruits such as pears (even when peeled), are good sources of fiber. Offer children wedges of seedless orange and apple. They have fiber that's lost when they're made into juice.

- The fruit and vegetable lists give columns of foods rich in vitamin A. Actually, these foods are rich in beta-carotene, a plant pigment that converts in the body to vitamin A.

- Generally, the more color a fruit (or vegetable) has, the more vitamins and minerals it contains.

- Vitamin A is necessary for normal growth. It also promotes good vision and strong tissues that are barriers to infections.

- Getting enough vitamin C is important for children because it is used to build bones, tissues, and blood. It protects tissues, promotes healing, and increases resistance to infections.

- For toddlers, avoid fruits with seeds. Pay special attention as toddlers eat dried or frozen fruits and cut firm fruits to be sure they don't choke on the hard bits of food.

- Bananas and avocados are favorites of young children because the fruits' textures are appealing. Both are rich in potassium and other minerals.

- Products marked "juice" must contain 100 percent juice. "Drinks," "ades," "punches," "cocktails," and other beverages may be little more than fruit-flavored sugar water.

- Giving a child juice made from concentrates is a good way to provide fluoride if your water supply is fluoridated.

- Juice is a food. Give it only once or twice a day so your child won't fill up on it and not eat other foods. Encourage plain water for thirst.

- Always peel fruits (and vegetables) to protect youngsters from pesticides. Young children are more sensitive to pesticide residues than older children and adults.

Vegetable Group

Recommended servings and typical serving sizes:

Ages 1 to 3: Three servings daily. Include one vitamin C–rich vegetable (or fruit) daily; plus 3 tablespoons vitamin A–rich vegetable (or fruit) every other day.

One serving = 2 to 3 tablespoons cooked or raw vegetables
= ¼ to ½ cup vegetable juice

Ages 4 to 5: Three servings daily. Include one vitamin–C rich vegetable (or fruit) daily; plus 4 tablespoons vitamin A–rich vegetable (or fruit) every other day.

One serving = ¼ to ½ cup cooked or raw vegetables
= ⅓ to ½ cup vegetable juice

BEST VEGETABLE CHOICES

VITAMIN C–RICH

Broccoli
Brussels sprouts
Cabbage
Cauliflower
Kale
Kohlrabi
Green and red
    sweet peppers
Mustard greens
Rutabaga
Potato (baked)
Snow pea pods
Sweet potato
Swiss chard
Tomato
Tomato juice
Vegetable juice

VITAMIN A–RICH

Asparagus
Beet greens
Broccoli
Brussels sprouts
Cabbage
Carrots
Carrot juice
Collard greens
Dandelion greens
Kale
Mixed vegetables (frozen)
Mustard greens
Peas
Romaine lettuce (or
    other deep-green lettuces)
Red sweet pepper
Pumpkin
Spinach
Sugar snap peas
Sweet potato
Swiss chard
Tomato
Tomato juice
Turnip greens
Vegetable juice
Winter squash

SECOND-BEST VEGETABLE CHOICES

Artichokes
Beets
Celery
Corn
Cucumbers
Eggplant
Garbanzo beans (chick-peas)
Green beans
Kohlrabi
Jicama
Leeks
Lentils

Lettuce (iceberg)
Lima beans
Mushrooms
Okra
Onions
Parsnips
Potato (boiled)
Radishes
Soybeans and tofu
   (soybean curd)
Sprouts
Summer squash
Turnip
Zucchini

WHAT YOU MAY NOT KNOW:

• To prevent children from choking, cook hard vegetables or cut them into long thin strips that are less likely to get stuck in tiny throats.

• Many vegetables are very good sources of dietary fiber (see the discussion on fiber, pages 50–51). Eating more vegetables aids elimination.

• Even if your child doesn't eat many vegetables, continue to offer them. Offer more fruit—it has nutrients similar to those in vegetables.

Starch Group (Breads, Cereal, Rice, and Pasta)

Recommended servings/serving sizes:

Ages 1 to 3: Four or more servings daily, including some whole-grain choices.

One serving = 2 to 3 crackers
$\qquad$ = $^1\!/_2$ slice of bread
$\qquad$ = $^1\!/_3$ cup cooked cereal, rice, or pasta
$\qquad$ = $^1\!/_3$ to $^1\!/_2$ cup dry cereal

Ages 4 to 5: Six servings daily, including some whole-grain choices.
$\quad$ One serving = 1 slice bread
$\qquad$ = 2 large or 4 small crackers
$\qquad$ = $^1\!/_2$ cup cooked cereal, rice, or pasta
$\qquad$ = $^1\!/_2$ to $^3\!/_4$ cup dry cereal

A word about our "Starch Choices" lists. . . .

Don't worry about giving your child some foods from the "Best Enriched/Fortified Starch Choices" list, such as white bread and sandwich buns. Enrichment replaces some of the nutrients lost during processing and fortification adds others. Some people say that white flour and products made with white flour are not nutritious. That is not true. It's just that whole grains are a bit better because they have more of some vitamins, minerals, and fiber. All starches are valuable sources of vitamins, minerals, and calories for children. Even the youngest child needs at least four servings from the starch group each day. It's best to offer a variety of selections from the list rather than four or more portions of the same starch. This is true of all other food groups, as well.

Too much fiber from whole grains, or bran added to foods, can interfere with the absorption of nutrients and make some children gassy. Do offer some whole-grain foods, so children become used to eating them. Whole grains become increasingly important in the diets of adolescents and adults.

There's more about grain foods in the section on fiber, pages 50–51. And everything you want to know about cereal for kids is included under "Breakfast Basics," pages 57 and 62–64.

WHOLE-GRAIN STARCH CHOICES

Barley	Rye bread
Brown rice	Rykrisp
Bulgar	Whole-grain breads

Corn tortilla
Millet
Oat bran
Oatmeal
Popcorn (for children
    over age 3)
Pumpernickel

Whole-grain cereals
Whole-grain crackers
Whole-grain wafers
Whole-grain Melba toast
Wheat germ
Whole wheat pasta

BEST ENRICHED/FORTIFIED STARCH CHOICES

Bagel, bialy
Bread sticks
Cereals (ready-to-eat,
    not too sweet)
Cooked cereals
    (all kinds)
Cornbread or muffins
English muffin
Flour tortilla
Hard rolls

Matzo
Melba toast
Noodles
Pasta
Raisin bread
Rusks
Spaghetti
White bread (enriched)
White rice
Zwieback

OTHER STARCH CHOICES

Biscuits
Bread stuffing
Fruit/nut bread
Graham crackers
French bread (unenriched)
Italian bread (unenriched)
Muffins (unenriched)
Oatmeal cookies
Pasta salad
Pretzels
Rice cakes

WHAT YOU MAY NOT KNOW:

• Even though pretzels have some salt, pretzel rods are a good crunchy snack that does not promote cavities.

• The Brown Rice Pudding (see page 297) and Bread Pudding (see page 296) recipes in this book contain a variety of nutritious ingredients in addition to the grain.

Meat and Other Protein Group

Recommended servings and typical serving sizes:

Ages 1 to 3: Two servings daily.
One serving = 1 ounce lean meat, fish, or poultry
= 1/4 cup cooked dried beans or peas
= 1 tablespoon peanut butter
= 1 egg

Ages 4 to 5: Two servings daily.
One serving = 2 ounces lean meat, fish, or poultry
= 1/3 cup cooked dried beans or peas
= 2 tablespoons peanut butter
= 1 egg

BEST ANIMAL-ORIGIN PROTEIN CHOICES

Chicken
Chicken livers
Eggs
Fish—fresh or canned
Lean beef, veal, pork, ham, lamb
Lean ground beef
Liver sausage, calves' liver
Reduced-fat cold cuts and franks (cut up for children under three)
Poultry-based cold cuts and franks (cut up for children under three)
Turkey

BEST PLANT-ORIGIN PROTEIN CHOICES

Almond butter
Black-eyed peas
Garbanzo beans
Kidney beans
Lentils
Lima beans
Peanut butter
Split peas
Tofu

OTHER PROTEIN CHOICES

Cold cuts
Duck, goose
Frankfurters (cut up for children under three)
Fried meat, poultry, or fish
Hamburger
Nuts (ground or finely chopped for children under three)

WHAT YOU MAY NOT KNOW:

• Eggs are a fine source of protein, vitamins, and minerals. Because of their texture and versatility, they are popular with young children. Many of the recipes in this book have one or two eggs in them, but often these eggs are distributed among six or more child-size servings of a particular food.

• Until children are almost three, their brain cells are still developing. They need protein for optimal brain growth. The meat and milk groups provide valuable protein. Most children in this country eat more than enough protein to meet these and other needs.

• The body absorbs iron and zinc from animal proteins particularly well. Iron is one of the nutrients that is most likely to be low in children's diets. Iron deficiency leads to fatigue and learning difficulties. Children who don't eat red meat regularly may have a hard time getting enough iron.

• If your child has a hard time chewing meat, prepare dishes with ground beef, lamb, or veal and serve tender meat cut into small pieces, with gravy or sauce to keep it moist.

• Most children love processed meats (luncheon meats, cold cuts, and hot dogs). Use them occasionally (once or twice a week), but don't make them the major meat source. For younger children, be sure to cut hot dogs into small, thin strips to prevent choking.

Vegetarian Diets

According to some estimates, 4 percent of adults in this country are vegetarians. A far greater number eat little or no red meat, though they eat poultry, fish, and dairy products. Are vegetarian diets adequate for preschoolers?

A vegetarian diet for a growing child must be very carefully planned if it is fully to meet needs for vitamins, minerals, protein, and calories. True vegan diets, which have no animal protein (meat, fish, poultry, eggs, milk, and other dairy products) are dangerous for growing children, especially during the first two years. Without dairy products, children cannot get enough calcium for bones and teeth and iron for red blood cells. Preschoolers who are given primarily fruits, vegetables, and grains may not get enough calories for their basic energy needs. If this happens, their body burns the valuable but limited protein for energy, instead of using it for brain and body growth.

A diet that includes milk, dairy products, and eggs can be combined with vegetable sources of protein to provide adequate amino acids necessary for growth.

If you are a vegetarian, you know about complementary proteins and combining foods to enhance protein availability. Whole grains and seeds will have to be ground or very finely chopped for children under age three. It's hard to be sure children are getting the nutrients they need. The corn and beans you offer may constitute a complete vegetarian protein, but only if both get eaten.

Here are some examples of recipes from this book with combined protein:

Legumes plus grains	Chick-Pea Salad (see page 120) in pita bread
	Brown Rice Salad with Peas (see page 122)
Legumes plus seeds/nuts	Cracked Wheat Garden (see page 121) with Sesame Wafers (see page 274)
Grains plus milk	Polenta (see page 170)
	Chewy Energy Bars (see page 270)
	Brown Rice Pudding (see page 297)
Grains plus egg	Savory Cheese Mini-tarts (see page 103)
	Sun and Clouds (see page 96)
	Orange French Toast (see page 260)

Young children do not absorb the nutrients in whole grains as well as adults. And whole-grain foods are bulky, so it's hard for some children to eat enough of them to meet their energy needs.

Give milk and milk products at meals, or add soy milk or tofu to casseroles and desserts to increase calcium. Creative use of legumes and seeds, such as our Banana Nut Sandwich (see page 234), offers variety as well as important nutrients.

While it is possible to provide adequate protein with a diet of mixed vegetable proteins, it is very hard for children who don't eat meat, fish, and poultry to get enough iron, zinc, and B-12 without taking supplements. Include vitamin C–rich foods at each meal to enhance iron absorption. Even if you don't eat meat, you may want to offer it to your child.

Parents' beliefs and religious convictions are major influences on the eating habits of many families. If you are a vegetarian, you should understand the implications of diet on a growing child. Read books on vegetarianism and consult a registered dietitian who has experience with vegetarian families.

·BEYOND THE· BASIC FOUR

N ow that we've presented the basics, it's time to tackle the tough nutrition issues: the headline-making stuff that gets your attention on television and in magazines and newspapers.

What follows is based on the most current research we could find at the time we were writing this book. In a number of instances, there is disagreement about what is best for young children. Our advice: Keep informed, talk with your doctor or a registered dietitian, and practice balance, variety, and moderation at the dinner table.

About Fat and Cholesterol

Some researchers believe that the beginnings of heart disease are in childhood and that young children should be given foods that are low in fat and cholesterol. Other researchers say that dietary efforts to prevent atherosclerosis should not start until adolescence. Still others contend that dietary changes should be made only by susceptible individuals.

If the experts can't agree, how can you make decisions about what's good to give your child to eat?

The doctor will determine whether or not to give your child a blood cholesterol test. This decision will be influenced in large part by your family's history of early heart disease and high serum cholesterol levels. Children of parents with high serum cholesterol levels are two and one-half times more likely to have high levels themselves.

A study by Doctors Richard E. Garcia and Douglas S. Moodie, published in the November 1989 issue of *Pediatrics*, found high serum cholesterol levels in 48 percent of children who had *no* family history of high cholesterol or premature heart attacks. Thus the authors of that study recommend that all children over three years old have a cholesterol test.

Over 90 percent of young children, whether tested or not, have normal serum cholesterol levels. If your child does have high cholesterol, you will want to arrange for nutrition counseling from a registered dietitian. Your child's special needs will make fat, saturated fat, and cholesterol control important in meal planning.

For children who are not "at risk" because of known high cholesterol levels or family history of premature heart disease, the general rule for fat and dietary cholesterol is *moderation*. Moderation can be achieved by offering a wide variety of foods, including foods that are moderate, rather than higher, in fat and cholesterol. Foods with moderate levels are sufficient for children's growth and energy needs.

To understand the issues of fat and cholesterol and put them into perspective, some basic fat facts are necessary.

Dietary fats are made up of different types of fatty acids—some are unsaturated, others saturated. These terms describe the chemical structure of the fatty acids that combine to form the fat. All forms of fatty acids contain the same number of calories. What's important to know is that most saturated fats tend to raise cholesterol level in blood—even more than cholesterol that's in food. And unsaturated fats may help lower blood cholesterol.

The two types of unsaturates have different chemical fatty-acid structures:

Monounsaturated: olive oil, canola oil, peanut oil and peanut butter, avocados, nuts and nut butter

Polyunsaturated: corn oil, safflower oil, sunflower oil, and soybean oil

Saturated fats are found primarily in meat, whole milk, cheese, butter, egg yolks, cream, lard, and tropical oils (coconut oil, palm kernel oil, and palm oil) that are used in prepared foods. Let's discuss these foods and how they relate to the needs of children.

Meat is an important food for youngsters because it is an excellent source of many important nutrients. To limit the amount of saturated fat and cholesterol, choose lean cuts of red meat, trim the visible fat, and avoid cooking methods that add fat.

After breast milk or formula, children should be given whole milk up to the age of two. The fat and cholesterol in it are positive factors in brain and nervous system development. After age two, the doctor may advise switching to 1 percent or 2 percent milk.

Cheese is also a valuable food because it has calcium. It's especially important for children who don't drink much milk. Give more low- and moderate-fat cheeses, such as cottage cheese, string cheese, Lorraine Swiss, ricotta, and mozzarella, and less high-fat cheese, such as Brie and cream cheese. It isn't necessary to buy dry cottage cheese. Cottage cheese with some cream has a moister consistency preferred by youngsters, and it's still considered a low-fat cheese.

You may want to substitute Neufchâtel or whipped or light cream cheese for regular cream cheese to give moderate rather than high-fat choices. Choose most cheeses from those that list 7 grams or less fat per ounce on the nutrition label.

By substituting margarine made with vegetable oil for butter or lard (in cooking or as a spread) and using dressings made with polyunsaturated and monounsaturated oils, you can reduce the amount of saturated fat and cholesterol you serve your family.

Tropical oils contain no dietary cholesterol but are more saturated than meat or butter—and they seem to increase cholesterol production in the body. When you read the ingredient panel on packaged foods, you will often see coconut oil, palm kernel oil, and palm oil. Make realistic judgments. If, for example, a cereal has only 1 gram of fat, and that fat is primarily a tropical oil, there is no need for concern. On the other hand, if you are considering crackers with 5 grams of fat, with a tropical oil listed high on the ingredient list, choose a different brand.

Cholesterol in food is a waxy, fatlike substance. It is found only in foods that come from animals—egg yolks, dairy products, meat, poultry, shellfish.

Egg yolks contain particularly high amounts of cholesterol—212 milligrams per large egg. But eggs are a very good source of protein, vitamins, and minerals for children. The American Heart Association recommendation (which is not age-specific) suggests no more than four egg yolks a week. Unless eggs are restricted for your child, serve eggs (or include them in cooked items) up to four times a week.

If egg yolks are restricted, use one whole egg and one egg white to replace two whole eggs or replace the eggs with a low-cholesterol substitute.

Fish, except for shellfish, which varies widely in cholesterol content, has less cholesterol than meat or poultry. Liver, kidneys, sweetbreads, and brains are very high in cholesterol.

Beware of foods labeled "no cholesterol." Read the label carefully, as these foods may be high in saturated fat. And for most people, including young people, saturated fat and the total amount of fat are more important than the amount of cholesterol in food.

From a practical standpoint, calories are lost when you substitute low-fat products. Young children need lots of calories in proportion to their weight. For example, a two- to three-year-old child weighing 40 pounds needs about 1,800 calories a day. His or her mother, who weighs 135 pounds, needs about 2,200 calories. At only one-third the weight of the mother, the child needs 82 percent of her calories. A *very* low-fat diet may not provide enough calories to meet growth needs. That's why we advocate a moderate fat intake. Fat contains more calories than carbohydrate or protein. Many children simply don't have the capacity (or hunger) to eat enough low-fat foods (fruit, vegetables, grains) to provide adequate calories for optimal growth and development.

As this book is written, a number of fat substitutes are in the final approval process by the Food and Drug Administration. We do not advise giving chemically derived fat substitutes to young children.

Reviews of the research indicate that fat substitutes may impair the absorption of some vitamins and minerals. As more is known about fat substitutes, this advice may change. The American Academy of Pediatrics has not yet issued a statement on them. Unless the Academy says it's okay, we say "don't."

Occasional high-fat foods, such as fried chicken, ice cream, or a brownie, can be part of a varied diet. But eating habits established during the formative years affect food choices throughout life. Your child can get adequate calories without eating a lot of hot dogs and fries.

Here are some ways to encourage moderate intake of fat in your preschooler's eating:

- Limit fried foods.
- Trim visible fat from meat.
- If you use processed meats, select ones with lower fat.
- For snacks, give fruits and vegetables or dairy products instead of chips and pastries.
- Suggest appropriate amounts of margarine, salad dressing, and sauce to put on food.

Fats/Oils Choices

(used moderately)

Ice cream (regular instead of very rich brands)
Margarine (from monounsaturated and polyunsaturated oils)
Mayonnaise
Neufchâtel (cream) cheese
Salad dressing
Vegetable oil (corn, safflower, sunflower, canola, olive, cottonseed)
Whipped cream cheese

Other Fats/Oils Choices

(used occasionally)

Butter
Corn chips, potato chips, and other fried snacks
Cream cheese
Fried foods
Gravy
Hydrogenated shortening
Ice cream (very rich)
Lard (may be in pie crusts)
Sour cream
Whipped cream

WHAT YOU MAY NOT KNOW:

• Do not try to severely restrict fat intake when feeding children. Do, however, pay attention to the amount and type of fat in foods.

• The recipes in this book use margarine as an ingredient instead of butter because margarines are high in unsaturated fats, while butter is high in saturates.

• Some bread products have considerable amounts of fat. Look at labels of frequently eaten foods, such as crackers, to see how much and what type of fat is used.

• Easy and healthful changes for the whole family include substituting margarine for butter, ice milk or frozen yogurt for rich ice cream, and fat-reduced cheeses for higher fat types.

Sugar and Sweeteners

Babies are born with a natural preference for sweetness. The early diet of sweet breast milk or baby formula perpetuates the innate preference. So don't be surprised if your child has a "sweet tooth."

A preference for sweet-tasting foods is not the nutritional original sin. Anthropologists say that our ancestors chose sweet foods because usually they were safe; bitter foods often were poisonous. Unknown foods with strange smells and sour or strong tastes were, and still are, received with suspicion.

To make foods more acceptable, we sometimes sweeten them. If a spoonful of sugar makes the medicine go down, as Mary Poppins said, it might also make the yogurt, cereal, and cranberries go down.

When we were doing market research on cookbooks for children, we noticed that a number of them used honey, brown sugar, molasses, and concentrated apple juice in place of white sugar. Don't be fooled! Nutritionally they are all about the same. All are sources of carbohydrate containing minimal vitamins, minerals, protein, or fiber. There is one food safety issue. Honey and liquid corn syrup should never be given to children under the age of one because they can carry spores of botulism that can be toxic to very young children.

Children rarely eat sugar unless it is used as an ingredient or a topping for cereal or fruit. While there are few nutritional benefits from sugar and other sweeteners in foods such as candy, frosting, and soft drinks, sweeteners sometimes keep very healthful company. Our recipe for Banana Cake (see page 306), for instance, contains whole wheat flour, bran, eggs, raisins, and bananas in addition to sugar.

Natural sources of sugar, such as juice (fructose) or milk (lactose), are better options than soft drinks because juices and milk provide some protective nutrients, too. Treats from a fruit bowl rather than the cookie jar make good nutritional sense. Try offering dried fruits as a sweet treat instead of candy. Just be sure that tooth-brushing follows sticky fruit snacks.

All forms of sugar, even those in wholesome foods such as fruit and milk products, contribute to cavities if they are in prolonged contact with teeth. By two and a half, most children have all of their primary teeth. These "baby teeth" are forerunners of permanent teeth, which begin to appear about age six. If baby teeth are eroded or lost, the permanent teeth cannot align properly.

Children should be drinking liquids from a cup by the time they are a year old. Giving milk or juice from a bottle at bedtime exposes the teeth to decay-causing bacteria over an extended period of time. Severe decay, called "nursing bottle syndrome," can erode young teeth. Children who suck on a bottle while lying down are also more likely to get ear infections.

A cavity is a bacterial infection of the tooth. For the infection to begin, there must be plaque, carbohydrate such as sugars or starches, and a susceptible tooth. The sugars and starches allow the bacteria in plaque to form acids. The sticky plaque holds the acid on the teeth for twenty minutes or more. After many such attacks, the enamel on teeth breaks down and a cavity occurs. Fluoride, often added to local water supplies, strengthens enamel and makes it less susceptible to decay. Children who drink water containing the right amount of fluoride from birth have up to 65 percent fewer cavities. When they are teenagers, 20 percent of them still will be cavity-free. If you live in a community without fluoridated water, the dentist or doctor may prescribe a daily fluoride supplement. The dentist may also periodically apply fluoride directly to the teeth.

Brushing teeth reduces plaque, one of the factors in this sequence. Brushing teeth after eating sugar- or starch-containing foods reduces the production of acid. How often the teeth are exposed to carbohydrate foods, the length of time these foods stay in the mouth, and the stickiness of the foods all play a role in tooth decay. Sugar-containing foods eaten as part of a meal are less harmful than between-meal sweets. The saliva produced during chewing of other foods and the liquids drunk with the meal help remove sugar from the teeth.

Adding a bit of sugar to certain foods such as cereal may encourage children to eat them. Unless they are overweight or have diabetes mellitus, preschoolers benefit from the calories they get from small amounts of sugar. Again, the guide is moderation. We do not encourage frequent eating of candy, sugared beverages, or gelatin desserts that are merely sugar. Instead, give foods that have some protein, vitamins, and minerals, in addition to the sugar.

But does sugar influence children's behavior? Most reports of sugar dramatically influencing behavior are based on anecdotes and informal observations. When scientific methods such as double-blind studies are used, these reports seldom are confirmed. In normal, healthy children, sugar intake appears to have a minimal influence on behavior.

Surprisingly, very few controlled studies on the subject have been published. Two of these studies, by R. J. Prinz and associates in 1980 and M. L. Lester and associates in 1982, suggest a possible link between sugar and behavior, but in neither case did sugar cause a child to become restless or achieve less in school. Another study, published by the Center for Brain Sciences and Metabolism Charitable Trust, was done with children who were hospitalized for severe behavioral disorders. In that study, changes related to sugar intake could be detected only by very sensitive techniques and trained observers.

In another study published by the same trust, children appeared calmer after a sugar load. It is true that some foods, including sugars, can affect the body's production of brain chemicals called neurotransmitters. Some evidence suggests that sugars and starches make certain people feel calm or sleepy.

Based on existing research, there are no firm conclusions about sugar and behavior. What many parents label "hyperactivity" may, in fact, be age-appropriate excitement and energy. If you think your child is hyperactive, see a qualified expert who can determine if your youngster has "attention deficit hyperactivity disorder" (ADHD), a condition with well-established diagnostic criteria.

Because sugar isn't an essential nutrient, it won't hurt to limit the amount you give your child, especially if you think he or she is sensitive to it. On the other hand, there is no scientific rationale for eliminating sugar from your child's food. In fact, obsessive sugar restriction is more likely to cause your child to become overly interested in forbidden sweets.

"Regular" as opposed to "diet" foods are best for most young children unless there is a specific medical reason to avoid sweeteners.

To provide moderate, but not excessive, amounts of sugar:

- Encourage your child to appreciate the natural sweetness of foods.
- Limit candy.
- Cut back on the amount of sugar you use in cooking.
- Look on ingredient panels on food labels. Foods with sugar or corn syrup as one of the top three ingredients are highly sweetened, since ingredients are listed in order of amounts used.
- Avoid heavily sweetened cereals, cookies, and snacks.
- Use juice-packed rather than syrup-packed canned fruit.
- Offer water rather than juice, soft drinks, or other sweetened beverages to a thirsty child.

Best Sugar/Sweets Choices

(used moderately)

Angelfood and sponge cake
Cakes or pies containing whole grains and/or fruits
Fruit or grain cookies
Fruit sorbets
Frozen fruit bars
Frozen fudge bars or pudding pops
Preserves, jam, jelly, fruit spreads
Molasses
Simple cookies
Sweetened cereals (fortified)

Other Sugar/Sweets Choices

(used occasionally)

Candy
Coffee cake, sweet rolls
Doughnuts
Flavored gelatin
Frosted cake
Pastries
Popsicles
Rich cookies
Sugar, brown sugar, honey, maple, corn, or pancake syrup

WHAT YOU MAY NOT KNOW:

• Some sugar increases the palatability of foods and provides needed calories for growing children.

• Strict refusal to permit sweets often backfires, causing an increased desire for them.

• Avoid positioning sweets as treats by including some in regular meals and snacks.

• Sweetened gelatin is just sugar, artificial color, and flavor. Add fruit to improve its nutritional profile.

• Never bribe children with sweets. If sweets are perceived as rewards, there may be a tendency to seek sweets in response to stress. This can create long-term weight control problems.

Shaking the Salt Habit

Before the age of two, children perceive bitter and sour tastes but are largely indifferent to salt (sodium). Baby food manufacturers removed the salt from their products several years ago when it became clear that the foods were seasoned to please the palates of adults, not babies. Research indicates that the amount of salt an adult prefers depends on what that person has become used to.

Sustained overuse of sodium can cause high blood pressure in sensitive individuals. Scientists do not agree on whether there are benefits to reducing sodium intake in people who are not salt-sensitive. Health experts advise limiting salt, especially in families where there is a history of high blood pressure. Almost all Americans eat far more sodium than they need anyway.

Adults need only 500 milligrams of sodium per day, one-year-old children need only 225 milligrams, and children ages two to five need only 300 milligrams each day. The amount needed is easily met, and often exceeded, by eating a varied diet, even with no added salt or foods processed with salt. Foods and beverages containing salt are the major sources of dietary sodium—all other sodium compounds and sodium-containing ingredients account for less than 10 percent of total sodium consumed.

For many children in the United States, iodized salt is a major source of iodine. Children who live in areas of the country where the iodine level in the soil is low should be monitored for iodine as part of regular physical checkups. Because iodine is an ingredient in most sanitizing compounds used to clean food production equipment, there are minute residues of iodine in many foods. As very little iodine is needed, this is enough to protect most adults and children from iodine deficiency.

The recipes in this book use small amounts of salt, far less than the amount added to many packaged and canned foods. The level of salt (sodium) in these recipes is acceptable for all family members, from both health and taste standpoints, but is not enough to promote a preference for salty foods.

If you or others at your family dinner table routinely add salt to foods, discriminating young diners will want some, too. "Because I don't use salt in cooking anymore, we have salt on the table," explains Maggie Powers, the mother of three young children. "But the adults control the salt shaker. If the kids want some, we 'waft' it over their food. Recently my daughter Jessica had a bite of meat from my plate and found it too salty. I hope this means we've succeeded in limiting her taste for salt."

To provide moderate salt intake:
- Encourage an appreciation for the natural flavor of foods.
- Use moderate amounts of salt in cooking.
- Put salt into pepper shaker, which usually has smaller holes.
- Provide snacks that are not highly salted.
- Avoid routine use of highly salted prepared and convenience foods, such as flavored pasta, rice mixes, and canned soups.
- Limit use of highly salted meat products, such as corned beef and salami.

Fiber

Fiber is the indigestible portion of edible plants. In the large intestine of humans, fiber works as a natural laxative, absorbing water and softening the stool. In the large intestines of little people, it takes less indigestible fiber to do the job than it does in a full-size human plumbing system.

When fiber absorbs water, it expands and gives a feeling of fullness. It may be necessary to limit fiber for children who have small appetites if they are to eat enough food to get adequate nutrients. On the other hand, adding high-fiber foods that are low in calories can be helpful for a child who is overweight.

Excessive fiber can interfere with absorption of important nutrients, such as calcium, iron, and zinc. A bran muffin or fiber-rich cereal is fine if eaten no more than once a day. But bran or other forms of fiber should not be added to children's foods. During the preschool years, it's more important that a child get adequate calcium and iron than large amounts of fiber.

Fiber is found in whole-grain breads and cereals, fruits, and vegetables. When you peel fruits and vegetables, as many health experts advise for young children, you remove a major source of fiber. You also limit fiber when feeding children under age three by not giving them seeds and nuts.

A child who is given too much fiber can have gas, cramps, bloating, and diarrhea. A child who gets too little can be constipated. Moderate amounts of fiber, along with water and other fluids, are the best way to prevent constipation. Gradually increase fiber in your child's diet as he or she gets older to encourage adequate fiber intake throughout life.

Good Fiber Choices for Children

Apples
Baked beans
Bananas
Barley
Bean burritos
Blueberries
Bran muffin
Broccoli
Brown rice
Brussels sprouts
Cabbage
Carrots
Cereal (with three or more
    grams of fiber per
    adult serving)
Chili with beans
Corn
Dried apricots, dates
Figs
Garbanzo beans

Kidney beans
Lentils
Lima beans
Oranges
Parsnips
Peanut butter
Pears
Peas
Potatoes
Prunes
Raisins
Raspberries
Strawberries
Sweet potatoes
Succotash
Tomatoes
Whole-grain crackers
Whole-grain muffins
Whole wheat bread
Winter squash

About Additives

Food additives are a mixed blessing. They allow us to buy bread that lasts a week instead of getting stale on the second day, and they allow us to select from a huge variety of food from around the world every day of the year. On the other hand, continued monitoring is necessary to ensure safety and avoid medical problems in individuals who are sensitive to particular additives.

The Food and Drug Administration (FDA) regulates additive use in commercial foods. Sugar, corn syrup, and salt are the most commonly used food additives. These and other additives play a valuable role in our food supply by:

- maintaining and improving nutritional value
- keeping foods fresh

- slowing microbial growth and keeping food from spoiling
- giving desired texture, flavor, and appearance
- aiding in processing and preparation

In 1973 Benjamin Feingold, M.D., an allergist, reported that approximately half of the hyperactive children he treated responded favorably when placed on a special diet that eliminated artificial colors, flavors, several antioxidants, and natural salicylates. But research in well-controlled studies, including a review by the National Institutes of Health, concluded that such dietary restrictions have a positive effect on very few children.

Increased attention and parent-child interactions making a child feel special, cared for, and loved contribute to the "effectiveness" of almost any type of dietary restriction. Well-controlled studies eliminate this variable.

Feingold's diet, as originally designed, is very restrictive and may not be nutritionally adequate. Elimination of foods with synthetic colors and flavors usually results in reducing the intake of processed and sugary foods—which is fine, as long as children get adequate calories from grains, lean meats, dairy products, and fresh fruits and vegetables.

If your child is hyperactive, or has other behavioral problems, consult your doctor and have a professional evaluation. Diet may not be the cause or the appropriate treatment.

Some children are sensitive to MSG (monosodium glutamate), sulfites, and FD & C Yellow #5, a food color. Allergy symptoms can follow eating a food containing one of these additives. Although rare, reactions can be severe. If your child is sensitive, read ingredient lists on food labels and avoid suspect substances. Your doctor or a registered dietitian can provide lists of foods containing these common allergens.

Sodium nitrite is used in processed meats, such as bacon, hot dogs, and sausage, to preserve color and prevent spoilage. The sodium nitrite is added to inhibit bacterial growth of dangerous botulinum. Cook bacon at low temperatures to avoid converting some of the nitrites to nitrosamines, which have been found to cause cancer. To limit nitrosamines, prepare bacon in the microwave and do not cook with bacon drippings.

Hot dogs and luncheon meats (cold cuts) are often favorites of children because they are flavorful, moist, and easy to chew. Occasional use is fine (no more than twice a week), but don't serve these foods on a daily basis. As well as containing nitrites and other chemical additives, bacon, hot dogs, and sausages such as bologna are all high in fat and saturated fat. There are far better choices to be found to provide protein for growing children.

Recipes from this book can replace many convenience foods that contain artificial colors, flavors, and chemicals used in processing. If you are concerned about additives, read ingredient lists on food packages and avoid those that contain the additives you find objectionable.

Generally, we advise using less highly processed foods for your child. We advocate "real" foods rather than highly processed packaged foods. Think "Mother Nature" when you shop. Real orange juice or frozen concentrate is a better choice than fortified orange-flavored drink. There are many healthful items in your neighborhood supermarket. You don't have to shop in a "health food" store.

With advances in food science, we see a growing array of sugar and fat substitutes in foods that we commonly eat. Often these substitutes are used to reduce calories. These substitutes should not be given to children one to five years of age; we do not know the long-term effects. As we have said, we suggest that you give your child "real" food and avoid chemically derived sugar and fat substitutes.

If you offer a variety of foods from each of the basic food groups each day, your child's nutritional needs are likely to be met. The key to it all is variety and positive attitudes toward healthful foods. While occasional use of a high-fat or very sweet food is fine, we are certainly not suggesting overloading your child's diet with fried, fatty, or highly sweetened foods, nor are we suggesting that these foods take the place of foods from the other food groups. Don't worry about an occasional stop at a fast-food restaurant, birthday parties, or holidays. These splurges will be offset by many well-planned regular meals and snacks and best-choice foods.

Safe Food

Young children are more vulnerable to food-borne illness than adults, so extra care must be taken to ensure that safe food is prepared, stored, and served.

Parents who are worried about food safety for their children have more reason to examine the way food is handled in their home than to be unduly concerned about additives.

Food Safety Rules

- Peel fresh fruits and vegetables before they are eaten.
- Refrigerate raw fish, meat, poultry, and dairy products.
- Wash (with soapy water) and rinse the cutting board, knife, sink, and counter surfaces after preparing raw poultry.
- Thoroughly cook eggs, poultry, and meat for children. Do not give them drinks or desserts made with uncooked eggs or use salad dressings made with raw eggs.
- Promptly refrigerate or freeze leftover foods. Do not let hot cooked foods cool at room temperature before refrigerating them.
- Discard foods that have been served or partially eaten. To avoid waste, serve small portions and freeze single-serve portions.
- If perishable foods are carried away from home, use an insulated pack.
- Be wary about food that is prepared under potentially unsanitary conditions, such as by street vendors or while traveling.

Throughout this book, there are repeated warnings about foods that can cause young children to choke. Bits of food, such as raisins, popcorn, nuts, hot dogs, or small sausages, can block tiny windpipes. To avoid a tragedy, an adult should always be present when preschoolers are eating, and children should not be allowed to run around while eating. For safety's sake, parents and caregivers should know the Heimlich maneuver.

SAFETY CHECK FOR CHILDREN UNDER THREE

- Avoid fruits with seeds, sunflower seeds, and popcorn.

- Slice grapes in half.

- Cut fruits, vegetables, and meat (especially hot dogs) into slender strips that will not get caught in a child's throat.

- Cook hard vegetables until soft.

- Give only smooth nut butters, not chunky types.

·FAMILY PLAN AND· SPECIAL-OCCASION MEALS

Most preschoolers need five or six meals a day: breakfast, lunch, dinner, and two or three snacks. The schedule can be tailored to meet individual preferences and family schedules.

Lisa's husband goes to work at 6:00 A.M., before the children are awake. Her son Elliott begins his day with a cereal and juice snack at 7:00 or 7:30. When his sister wakes up at 9:00 or 9:30, Elliott, Erin, and Mom have a big breakfast together. Lunch is served at about 1:00 P.M., after naps.

On days when Maggie Powers works away from home, the children's first meal is sometimes at the baby-sitter's house. Maggie and her husband, who both counsel patients in an office in their home, have dinner with their three children at 4:00 or 4:30 in the afternoon before evening appointments. The children may have one or even two snacks before bedtime.

Tony and Sharon Zilich used to have daily negotiations about when—or if—they would have dinner together. Now, dinnertime is a regular 6 o'clock appointment with their daughters, Emily and Claire. "It's a commitment that we take seriously," Sharon says. "The meetings with clients and attention to projects can generally be scheduled before or after dinner, if we make an effort to do so," she explains. For some families this just isn't possible.

Making time for family meals may require new strategies—

family breakfast, late dinner and delayed bedtime, or main meal at midday (at home or work) and light supper together before evening activities.

While we recommend healthful home-prepared meals as the norm, there are some alternatives available for occasional use or when your child is the only one eating. For example, a new line of shelf-stable entrées under the brand name My Own Meal is specifically designed to meet the nutritional needs and taste preferences of young children. These entrées are useful for traveling, camping, and day care because they do not require refrigeration and can be quickly heated in a microwave or in hot water. Children enjoy the saucy protein, grain, and vegetable combinations.

Regardless of how much you know about food and nutrition, meal preparation takes planning. Jane Voichick, Ph.D., a colleague of Anne and Mary's and currently a professor at the University of Wisconsin, has an impressive ten-page résumé—and a family to feed. For years Jane has used the monthly menu in *Women's Day* magazine to plan meals for her family.

A big freezer is almost essential. On weekends Mary prepares double batches of foods—some for quick, after-work midweek meals and the rest to freeze. Barbara freezes many of the foods she prepares for her boys in single servings for future meals. "If kids don't like something when you first make it, freeze what's left (in small portions) and offer it again a week or two later," she advises. When you discover favorite recipes in this book, make and freeze extra.

"I find the food group plan a helpful guide," says Maggie Powers. "We have a picture of the food groups on our refrigerator." If you regularly serve a variety of healthful foods from the basic groups, you don't have to worry about hot dogs at the zoo, fruit punch at the baby-sitter's, or occasional meals at fast-food restaurants.

The eight days of menus beginning on page 58 give you an idea of what a week's worth of children's meals looks like. The recipes included in this book are marked with an asterisk. The daily offerings meet the food group criteria. An extra day of menus is included just in case several "unfavorites" are suggested on the same day. Feel free to mix and match—just check to see that you have enough foods from each food group. The menu plan has breakfast, midmorning snack, lunch, afternoon snack, dinner, and evening snack. The sequence may vary according to the schedule best for you and your child. Although three snacks a day are included, you may only want to serve two. Adjust portion sizes for your child's age and appetite, and give water when no beverage is listed.

Reports say that many preschoolers don't drink enough water. Young children may not realize that they are thirsty. Give water often, rather than juice, milk, soft drinks, or sweetened beverages to quench thirst. Kids need to learn to appreciate unsweetened plain water. Offer it frequently, especially on hot days or if a child has been sick with diarrhea or vomiting.

Breakfast Basics

Anne Boleyn fed her daughter, the future Queen Elizabeth I, goose pie and rabbit for breakfast. Anne washed hers down with a pint of ale; her kids presumably had cider. Thomas Jefferson served chicken hash and braised partridges at his breakfast table.

The Mendoza children, who lived across the street from Anne Hunt's family in Chicago, had mashed potato–filled flour tortillas in the morning. And Rachel Hess liked tapioca pudding before school. Breakfast is not what but *when* you eat.

By morning, ten or twelve hours have elapsed since a child's last meal. Children need breakfast to boost their blood sugar. A nutritious breakfast provides carbohydrate for quick energy (especially for the brain); protein to get the day's cell-building under way; fats for fuel; and vitamins and minerals to spark all this activity. Studies show that children perform better when they have had breakfast.

Iron-fortified cereal is an important source of iron for preschoolers. As mentioned, a large majority of children one to five years old have iron intakes below the standard. Iron-deficiency anemia has been reported in 22 percent of all American preschoolers. Children with iron-deficiency anemia have decreased attention span, attentiveness, persistence, and voluntary activity.

The richest source of dietary iron is red meat, but few children, especially younger ones, eat very much meat. There are exceptions: As a toddler Leslie Hess banged her spoon on her high chair demanding "More meat!" When she was three years old, she astonished her grandmother by polishing off seven tiny grilled rib lamb chops at a sitting.

	DAY 1	DAY 2
Breakfast	Pineapple Juice *Daddy's Jelly Omelet Whole Wheat Toast/ 　Margarine	Orange Sections Oatmeal with Raisins Milk
Snack	*Cookie Cutter 　Cheeses Fresh Seedless Purple 　Grapes	*Pumpkin Muffin Cottage Cheese
Lunch	*Chick-Pea Salad in 　Pita Pocket Carrot Sticks/Pepper 　Rings Milk	*Popeye Soup/Crackers *Veal Loaf Sandwiches 　with Lettuce Milk
Snack	*Vegetarian Pizza	*Baked Tomato 　Custard
Dinner	*Foil-Cooked Lamb Roasted Potato Cuts Enriched Bread/ 　Margarine Sliced Peaches Milk	*Grandma Nettie's 　Chicken Parslied Bowtie 　Noodles *Orange Spiced Carrot 　Coins Rye Bread/Margarine Cranapple Juice
Snack	*Frozen Banana Pops Graham Crackers	*Brown Rice Pudding Milk

	DAY 3	DAY 4
Breakfast	Cantaloupe Wedge *Sun and Clouds Milk	Fresh Pineapple 　Chunks *French Waffles/Maple 　Syrup Milk
Snack	*Baked Sweet Potato/ 　Yogurt Topping	Frozen Fruit Bar Vanilla Wafers
Lunch	*Tuna and Confetti 　Corn Salad 　Sandwich Cucumber Slices Enriched Bread/ 　Margarine *Oatmeal Rocks Mixed Fruit Juice	*Vegetable Omelet Cherry Tomatoes Whole Wheat Bread/ 　Margarine *Banana Cake Milk
Snack	*Bagel/Vegetable 　Cream Cheese	*Quick Mushroom 　Barley Soup *Cheese Crouton 　Strips
Dinner	*Reina's Grandma's 　Pretty Neat Sloppy 　Joes on Bun *Orange and Green 　Salad Milk	*Swordfish and 　Nectarine en 　Brochette Boiled New Potatoes Green Beans *Creamy Coleslaw White Grape Juice
Snack	*Five-Minute Berry 　Ice Cream	Fresh Strawberries Frosted Fortified 　Wheat Cereal Milk

	DAY 5	DAY 6
Breakfast	Applesauce Raisin Toast/Margarine Grilled Ham Slice Milk	Fortified Oat Cereal Sliced Bananas Milk
Snack	*Banana-Blueberry Muffin Milk	Lemon Yogurt Pretzel Rods

Lunch	*Spaghetti with Rich
	  Tomato Sauce
	Green Salad Dressing
	Garlic Bread
	Fresh Seedless Green
	  Grapes
	Milk
		*Bean Tortilla Roll-ups
		Sliced Sweet Peppers
		  and Cucumbers
		Pear Nectar

Snack	*Fresh Vegetables/Golden Dippy Sauce	*Fruit Gelatin Surprise

Dinner	*Basil-Mustard Pork
	Steamed Rice
	*Sweet and Sour Red
	  Cabbage
	Tangerine Juice
		*Herbed Steak Package
		Mashed Potatoes/
		  Gravy
		*Spinach Fingers
		Whole Wheat Bread/
		  Margarine
		*Cherry Clafouti
		Milk

Snack	*Fruit and Nut Balls Graham Crackers	Fresh Apple Wedges Open-faced Grilled Cheese Sandwich

	DAY 7	DAY 8
Breakfast	Citrus Cup Toasted English Muffin Peanut Butter Apple Butter Milk	Tangerine Juice *Buckwheat Waffles Blueberries Milk
Snack	Chicken Noodle Soup Crackers	Vegetable Juice Cocktail String Cheese
Lunch	*Cheese "Blintzes" Strawberry Jam Tomato Wedges Milk	*Birthday Party* *Speared Poultry *Crispy Potato Fingers Steamed Pea Pods Birthday Cake Frozen Chocolate Yogurt Lemonade
Snack	*Bread Pudding Milk	Honeydew Melon Balls or Mango Slices
Dinner	Cranberry Juice Cocktail *Turkey Picatta (or Veal Picatta) Carrot Coins Steamed Broccoli *Pear Sherbet	*King Salmon Noodle Pudding Peas Stuffed Celery Enriched Bread/ Margarine Milk
Snack	Dried Apricots/Dates/ Popcorn	*Peanut Butter Chocolate Chip Cookie Milk

Even though most parents stop giving "instant baby cereal," such as Gerber's oatmeal or Beechnut rice cereal, when their child begins eating table food, these cereals are recommended for children up to age two because of their iron content. A great deal of research is under way to identify the most absorbable form of iron to add to these cereals. Continue to offer these instant cereals to your toddler. They are quick and easy to prepare in single portions, and they're lower in sodium than adult instant cereals. Baby cereal is used in some of the recipes in this book.

You can boost iron absorption at any meal or snack by serving a source of vitamin C. Serve fresh fruit or fruit juice with cereal. Orange, grapefruit, and tangerine juices are popular at the breakfast meal and are rich in vitamin C. Cantaloupe and strawberries are other excellent sources. The vitamin C bonus also boosts the absorption of iron from enriched bread, toast, and muffins.

Food tastes of four-year-old children are influenced by television watching, research shows. And the most frequent requests stimulated by television advertising are for presweetened breakfast cereals. Some of these cereals are named after or endorsed by cartoon characters or sports figures. To appeal to parents, cereal companies fortify these cereals with extra vitamins and minerals.

To make a cereal taste good, most of us add some sugar or fruit for sweetening. If you add one level teaspoon of sugar to your bowl of cereal, you are adding 4 grams of carbohydrate (16 calories) from sugar. A rounded teaspoon adds 7 or 8 grams. Ironically, some parents who are adamantly against presweetened cereals find it acceptable to add sugar from the sugar bowl to an unsweetened cereal.

In the local supermarket, we found twenty-four cereals that had more than one *tablespoon* (12 grams of sugar) per serving. These are more like candy than cereal! Count these (if used) on your sweets list—sort of a grain-enriched sweet, similar to a cookie.

Cereals typically have more than one kind of carbohydrate sweetener. The total is listed on a separate carbohydrate label as "sucrose and other sugars." These sweeteners are given in order, from most to least, on the ingredient list. And don't be fooled into thinking that cereal sweetened with honey or brown sugar is better for your child! Reread the section on sugars and sweeteners in the previous chapter to get the truth about that.

Keep in mind that a young child's portion is half of the standard adult portion. One ounce of most dry cereals measures ¾ to 1 cup.

```
┌─────────────────────────────────────────────────────────┐
│                                                           │
│              BOUNTIFUL GRAIN CEREAL                       │
│                 (1-ounce serving)                         │
│     Starch and related carbohydrate        12 grams      │
│     Sucrose and other sugars                 9 grams      │
│     Dietary fiber                            2 grams      │
│     Total carbohydrate                      23 grams      │
│                                                           │
└─────────────────────────────────────────────────────────┘
```

A cereal with a carbohydrate labeling panel such as the one shown above will provide less than 5 grams of sucrose and other sugars in a ½-ounce child-size portion. That's equal to a little more than 1 teaspoon. Dietitian Maggie Powers thinks that's too much. She won't buy cereal for her family that lists more than 5 grams for the full portion.

Some parents have rather creative solutions to the sugared-cereal dilemma.

• Serve whole-grain, unsugared cereal mixed with a small amount of sugared cereal.

• Melinda Maryniuk, a registered dietitian, collects coupons for cereals that have her stamp of approval. Then it's up to her four-year-old son to find the cereal on the shelf that matches the coupon.

• Put a tiny spoon in the sugar bowl and let your child take one or two spoonfuls. The total will be equal to about 1 measuring teaspoon.

• Fill a salt shaker with granulated sugar and let your child shake sugar on the cereal.

• Buy individual packets that contain ½ or 1 teaspoon of sugar.

If some sweetening is what it takes to get your preschooler to eat fortified cereal, it's well worth the extra calories. Reduce potential tooth decay by establishing a routine of brushing after breakfast. Remember that sugar-substitutes (nonnutritive sweeteners), such as Equal or Sweet 'n Low, are not recommended for children unless there is a clear medical reason for eliminating sugar.

Some cereals also include added fat as an ingredient. If the nutrition panel says the cereal has only 1 gram of fat, there is little reason for concern about what kind of fat or oil is used. If there are more than several grams, look at the types of fats and oils on the ingredient list. Coconut oil and palm kernel oil are sometimes added to keep cereal crispy and to prevent fruit from clumping together. Many cereals are available that do not contain significant amounts of these saturated fats, and they are better choices for family use.

Cereals are a favorite food of most young children. Many are nutritious and quick and easy to serve. Keep cereal handy, not just for breakfast but to give as a meal or snack. The cereal-fruit-milk combination offers key nutrients kids need in a form they like and with virtually no preparation time.

Snacks

Too bad there's not another name for "snacks"; the word has come to have such a negative connotation. That's because so many snacks have little nutritional value, and snacking tends to be unconscious, irregular eating. Try a new definition for "snack": a small quantity of healthful food eaten at a scheduled time between main meals.

For many adults, limiting calories is a positive nutrition action, and because many snacks are high in calories, cutting down on snacks may be a goal. But for children with high energy needs, high activity levels, and small appetites, getting enough calories takes more than three meals a day. Even children who are overweight need more than three meals a day to satisfy hunger and meet physical needs. For overweight children, low-calorie, nutrient-dense snacks are best.

And it isn't just calories that kids need; they need protein, vitamins, and minerals, too. In a growing child's diet, there is little room for foods that supply nothing more than calories.

Plan snacks, choosing foods that fit into the total day's food plan. Generally, offer a snack no sooner than two hours after a main meal or no closer than two hours before the next main meal. But if dinner is an hour away and you have a crabby, hungry child, a piece of fruit or a slice of bread can stem the hunger tide. If the time between main meals is long, serve two snacks. The important thing is that the snack not interfere with the next meal.

Snacks don't have to be served at the table, but children shouldn't be allowed to wander around while eating. For variety, have a snack picnic outdoors or on a small cloth or rug inside. Invite dolls and stuffed animals to sit at the small table and have a tea party snack.

When Anne's grandchildren have a snack, they have to sit down—somewhere. If they get up, the food is taken away. At Nan and Grandpa's house, Elliott likes to pull a small antique chair up to the living-room coffee table for his snack. Adults should have the final say as to where, as well as when and what, children eat.

Even though it's a common occurrence these days, think twice about serving snacks or meals in front of the television. This practice sets up habits that may contribute to the mindless eating and consumption of excess calories that can lead to obesity.

Ellyn Satter says, "Above all, don't allow television at mealtime. It profoundly interferes with family social time and with children's eating." She goes on to tell of research at Harvard University showing that children who spend more time in front of the television are fatter. Why? Maybe because of inactivity, the increased reminders to eat, or the decrease in metabolism from the hypnotic effects of television watching.

According to the research of Dr. William H. Dietz, Jr., a pediatrician at New England Medical Center, and Stephen L. Gortmacher, Ph.D., at the Harvard School of Public Health, watching television may reduce the time spent in activities that burn energy. In the long run, television viewing promotes eating the foods advertised, and children increase their attempts to influence food purchases.

A habit of TV watching is hard to break as children reach school age. Some studies of school-age children have found that the children who watch violence on television are more aggressive. School performance tends to decrease as hours of TV watching increase.

Preschoolers need structure and limits. Establish appropriate limits for television, just as you do for eating. In between, encourage active and creative play to help maximize the child's physical and intellectual development. It takes more than food to make a healthy child!

HEALTHY SNACK CRITERIA

- Takes place at a designated time and place.

- Satisfies hunger but does not keep child from eating at regular mealtime.

- Contributes to total day's need for foods from the food groups.

- Includes healthful food choices.

More than any other meal, snacks come under attack by dentists. It isn't just sugar that the dentists abhor, but starches and sticky foods. To reduce the chances of tooth decay from snacks:

- Serve a beverage with each snack.
- Offer cheese, which helps counter the effects of acid produced by bacteria in plaque.
- Avoid foods that stay in the mouth for a long time, such as hard candy and taffy.
- If you give snacks (including juice or milk) at bedtime, be sure your child brushes his or her teeth before going to sleep.
- Brush teeth after sticky foods and before bedtime.

Dessert and Other Goodies

The healthiest approach to dessert is to make it a part of the regular meal plan. The dessert recipes in this book are made with ingredients from the food group lists.

Don't offer dessert as a "reward" for eating the rest of the meal. To keep dessert in perspective, Ellyn Satter advises serving a portion right along with the meat and vegetables, rather than making it the grand finale. If your child wants to eat dessert and nothing else, you can say, "If you are still hungry, eat more meat or vegetables." And don't position frosted cakes or chocolate desserts as more "special" than fresh fruit or pudding.

Parents and caregivers, not preschoolers, buy candy, cookies, pastries, and rich ice cream. If you don't want your kids to eat these foods, don't have them readily available. If the baby-sitter brings candy, or a neighbor or grandparent gives your son or daughter a doughnut, avoid making it a big deal. That can elevate the food to a position of special value.

Cookies are a favorite snack of many young children. This book offers a variety of cookies that contain healthful ingredients and have lower levels of fat and sugar than many commercial varieties. Good packaged-cookie choices include fig bars, gingersnaps, graham crackers, vanilla wafers, and some animal crackers. Look at the ingredient lists and choose ones made without lard or tropical oils.

Party Time!

Halloween and other holidays are a challenge, but traditions are important, too. Barbara hosts an annual Halloween open house. She hires teenagers to help with crafts and games. One year she arranged for a special visit from Batman. By having the party at her house, she controls what food is served. Some of her Halloween treats are included in the recipe section of the book. Cheese ghosts and moons and black bread cats and bats shaped by cookie cutters were big hits! Another trick is to limit trick-or-treating time so that the cache of treats is not overwhelming. For safety's sake, an adult should inspect treats before anything is eaten. A day or two of extra candy and treats has no long-term impact. How about a special new trick-or-treat toothbrush and a brand-new tube of fluoride sparkle-gel toothpaste?

To a child, a birthday is the very best holiday. And what's a birthday without a birthday cake? You don't have to serve tofu loaf to keep a party healthy. Try our Carrot Cake (see page 307) or Banana Cake (see page 306) recipe with Cottage Cheese Frosting (see page 310) or Angel Cake (see page 309) with fresh strawberries and frozen yogurt. Older children will enjoy individually wrapped ice cream sandwiches made from Chocolate Tile Bars (see page 271) and ice cream or frozen yogurt. Let the birthday boy or girl help plan the menu and prepare the food. Four- and five-year-olds can even help decorate the cake!

Believe it or not, children will eat healthful food even at a birthday party! Keep the menu simple, with foods everyone will recognize, such as raw vegetables with Golden Dippy Sauce (see page 225), fresh fruit slices, pizza, Speared Poultry (see page 189), or finger sandwiches.

Plan a quiet activity before the food is served. Then seat the children around a table. Offer enough different foods so that each child will find something he or she likes. But if a young guest doesn't eat anything but cake, don't be offended. Eating isn't the reason for the party.

Feeding the Body, Mind, and Spirit

This book gives you guidelines for preparing and serving nutritious meals to your child. It tells you how to encourage eating behavior that will contribute to healthy attitudes about food throughout your son or daughter's life.

And remember, mealtimes can foster family unity and traditions, too. Dinner-table memories last longer than lectures about nutrition.

Healthy
Head Start
Recipes

·NOTES FROM· THE KITCHEN

L et me take off my apron and introduce myself. I'm Barbara Stone. I am a professional recipe developer. For many years I worked with cookbook author and free-lance writer Camille Stagg. I helped her develop and test recipes for articles published in *Woman's Day*, *Cook's Magazine*, *1000 Ideas*, *The Garden Gourmet*, and the *Chicago Tribune* newspaper. And we provided some food service ideas for Midway Airlines.

Since childhood, I've enjoyed preparing food. My mother was a good cook and encouraged my early attempts at creative cooking. But I didn't start out working in the food field.

I have an undergraduate degree in psychology from Brandeis University and a master's degree from the University of Chicago's School of Social Service Administration. After several years as a social worker, I went into personnel management.

But then I went to France and was absolutely smitten by the great chefs and their foods. This inspired me to take courses in food and nutrition at Mundelein College in Chicago, interspersed with "study" trips to France and Italy. A highlight of my training was an opportunity to work with Chef Dieter Hanig of Hilton International's test kitchen at New York's World Trade Center.

My interest in nutrition increased during my pregnancy with my first son, David (who is now six). When David started eating table food, I began cooking special things for him. I wanted him to eat healthful foods and to experience the wonderful diversity of tastes and textures and colors in foods. At the family dinner table, my husband, Bob, and I introduced David to the foods we enjoy: grilled fish and poultry, creative vegetable combinations, fine cheeses, artichokes, caviar, squid . . . and David loved it all!

David's brother, Michael, who is now two, often doesn't enjoy what David likes. And David doesn't like to eat everything he did when I first began this project. But I keep cooking—because I am committed to giving the boys healthful foods and because I like to cook. Tasting food is a wonderful experience, and preparing and sharing meals is an important part of our family life.

When creating a new dish, I write down the recipe, just as if I am developing a recipe for a magazine or newspaper. The recipes of foods I made for David and Michael became the nucleus of *A Healthy Head Start*. Friends who had children the same ages as mine encouraged me to put the recipes together into a book. I realized that feeding preschoolers involved more than preparing food for them. Mary Abbott Hess and Anne Hunt were just what I needed to provide sound nutrition information and practical feeding advice to go along with my recipes.

Mary reviewed the recipes from a nutritional perspective. She evaluated them based on the needs of *healthy* children, ages one to five. If your child has a medical problem, such as diabetes or allergies, ask a registered dietitian to help you adapt our recipes.

Change recipes to meet your child's needs. For example, omit nuts and seeds, or grind them until smooth, in dishes for toddlers. When a recipe calls for milk, use the type of milk suggested by your child's doctor.

The recipes that follow offer both you and your child opportunities to explore wonderful food tastes and textures. Don't reject a Blueberry and Spinach Omelet until you've tried it! After all, it won high praise from David, Michael, and their friends.

Providing healthful food is a way of expressing love to your child. These recipes were created with love. Serve them with warmth and caring and your child will have a healthy head start.

·SOUPS·

·Soup Recipes·

Chicken Noodle Soup
Mushroom Barley Soup
15-Minute Fish Chowder
Vicki's Pool of Vegetables
Jellied Soup
Popeye Soup
Thick Beet Borscht
Carrot Soup
Soup in a Shell

Soup is a wonderful way to get children to eat their vitamins and minerals. It's also a good way to use up leftovers.

Make your own broth or stock, or used canned varieties or low-sodium bouillon in recipes calling for broth. You can freeze broth in an ice cube tray, then take just what you need for a recipe.

Experiment with the temperature at which you serve soup. Most children like it lukewarm. Toddlers can manage soup more easily if it's served in a cup—a little at a time, until they get the hang of it.

Many of these recipes are good participative activities. It really doesn't matter if the vegetables end up in irregular shapes and sizes—and nothing tastes as good as "handmade" soup on a cold day!

· Chicken Noodle Soup ·

Chicken Noodle Soup is most children's favorite. For an even quicker version, use leftover vegetables or just peas and cooked noodles. If you don't have cooked noodles, use Oriental noodles that cook in only three minutes.

1 quart (4 cups) chicken broth
2 large carrots, peeled and diced
2 small turnips, peeled and diced
$3/4$ cup peas
1 cup cooked noodles, any shape
$1/4$ cup diced, cooked chicken

1. In a medium-size saucepan, bring broth to a boil.
2. Reduce to a simmer and add carrots and turnips. Cook over very low heat for 20 minutes.
3. Add peas and continue cooking over low heat for 10 minutes.
4. Add noodles and chicken and heat through.

Yield: 5 to 6 cups

· Mushroom Barley Soup ·

This soup has always been a "comfort food" in the Stone family. In its original version, it took all day to make. If you like a thicker soup, add more barley. Barley is an underused, complex carbohydrate with a texture that will intrigue young diners.

1 quart (4 cups) beef broth
3 tablespoons barley
2 carrots, peeled and diced
3/4 cup green beans, trimmed and cut into 1/2-inch
    pieces
2 cups thinly sliced mushrooms

Optional: 1/4 cup diced, cooked beef or veal

1. In a medium-size saucepan, bring broth to a boil.
2. Reduce heat to a simmer. Add barley and cook over low heat for 30 minutes.
3. Add carrots, green beans, and mushrooms. Cook over low heat for an additional 30 minutes.
4. Add cooked meat, if desired.

Yield: 5 to 6 cups

· 15-Minute Fish Chowder ·

This has been Michael's favorite soup since he first started eating table foods. It's really good on a cool day with bread, cheese, and fruit.

1 tablespoon vegetable oil
1 small red potato, peeled and diced
2 carrots, peeled and diced
1/2 small onion, diced
3 cups fish or chicken broth
1 cup cooked rice
1/2 pound scrod or other flaky, white, mild fish, cut into bite-size pieces
Salt and pepper to taste

1. In a medium-size saucepan, heat oil. Add potato, carrots, and onion and cook over medium heat 5 minutes.
2. Add broth and cook for 5 minutes, until vegetables are softened.
3. Add rice and fish. Cook for 5 minutes, until fish is flaky.
4. Season and serve.

Yield: 4 cups

·Vicki's Pool of Vegetables·

This recipe makes enough for the whole family. If it becomes too thick after standing, just add some hot water or broth. You can strain the leftover soup and use the broth to make Jellied Soup (see page 81).

1½ tablespoons vegetable oil
1 large onion, chopped
2 stalks celery, chopped
3 carrots, peeled and chopped
1 can (28 ounces) whole tomatoes
5 cubes vegetable bouillon plus 2 quarts (8 cups)
    boiling water or chicken broth
2 tablespoons frozen orange juice concentrate
¼ cup small pasta (alphabets, pastina, stars, orzo)
2 turnips, peeled and diced
2 parsnips, peeled and diced
1½ cups fresh green beans, trimmed and cut into
    ½-inch pieces
1 tablespoon chopped fresh parsley
1 teaspoon dried basil, or 1 tablespoon minced
    fresh basil
1 teaspoon dried oregano, or 1 tablespoon minced
    fresh oregano
⅛ teaspoon pepper
¾ cup frozen peas
2 cups fresh spinach, well washed and coarsely
    chopped

1. In a large pot, heat oil. Add onion, celery, and carrots and sauté over medium heat until soft but not brown, about 10 minutes.
2. Add tomatoes and juice from can; crush tomatoes with a spoon.

3. Add bouillon and broth, orange juice, pasta, turnips, parsnips, green beans, parsley, basil, oregano, and pepper. Simmer over medium-low heat for 20 minutes.
4. Add peas and spinach and continue to cook over low heat for 5 minutes.

Yield: 10 cups

· Jellied Soup ·

This is a good way to use leftover vegetable soup, and it makes a healthful, fun finger food.

2 packages (2 tablespoons) unflavored gelatin
2 cups strained vegetable broth (see Vicki's Pool of Vegetables, page 80), or 1 cup V-8 juice and 1 cup broth

1. In a medium-size bowl, sprinkle gelatin.
2. Pour 1 cup cold broth or juice over gelatin and let it sit for 1 minute.
3. Bring 1 cup broth to a boil and pour into gelatin. Stir until gelatin dissolves.
4. Pour into a dish, mold, or mini-muffin cups. Refrigerate until hard, at least 2 hours.

Yield: 20 1¹/₂-inch cubes

· Popeye Soup ·

ᎧᎧᎧᎧᎧᎧᎧᎧᎧᎧᎧᎧᎧᎧᎧᎧᎧᎧᎧᎧᎧᎧᎧ

Incredibly rich in vitamins and iron, this soup is both nourishing and delicious. To make a thinner version, add more water or broth. Serve warm or cold with black bread or pumpernickel crackers.

$\frac{1}{2}$ cup water or broth
3 cups fresh spinach, well washed and stems
  removed
1 cup fresh parsley, stems removed
1 clove garlic, peeled and minced
1 cup mashed or diced cooked potatoes
1 cup plain low-fat yogurt
$\frac{1}{4}$ cup shredded beets or carrots for garnish

1. In a medium-size saucepan, bring water or broth to a boil.
2. Add spinach and parsley. Simmer over medium heat for 2 minutes.
3. Transfer contents of saucepan to food processor or blender. Add garlic and process until smooth.
4. Add potatoes and yogurt. Process until just blended.
5. Garnish each serving with shredded beets or carrots.

Yield: 1$\frac{1}{2}$ cups

· Thick Beet Borscht ·

Most children adore naturally sweet, colorful beets. Fresh beets are especially tasty, and you can also serve the iron-rich beet greens, if they are fresh and not wilted. If you substitute 1 cup canned, drained beets for the fresh beets, start the recipe at step 2. A bib or napkin around your child's neck protects clothes from stubborn-to-remove beet stains.

1 cup diced, peeled, fresh beets (about 3 small),
   greens removed
1 large green onion or leek, chopped
1 cup water
1½ cups beef or vegetable broth
1 cup chopped beet greens
1 teaspoon brown sugar
1 teaspoon vegetable oil
1 teaspoon cider vinegar
1 cup plain low-fat yogurt
Plain low-fat yogurt for garnish
Fresh or dried dill weed for garnish

1. In a medium-size saucepan, combine beets and onion. Cover with water. Bring to a boil and cook over medium heat for 10 minutes.
2. Add broth, greens, sugar, oil, and vinegar. Cook over medium heat for 15 minutes. Remove from heat.
3. Puree beet mixture in a food processor or blender.
4. Pour mixture into a nonmetal container and stir in yogurt. Chill several hours or overnight, until cold and very thick.
5. To serve, spoon about ⅓ cup soup into a small bowl or cup; garnish with a spoonful of yogurt and a sprinkle of dill weed.

Yield: 2½ cups

·Carrot Soup·

ᵔᵔᵔᵔᵔᵔᵔᵔᵔᵔᵔᵔᵔᵔᵔᵔᵔᵔᵔᵔᵔᵔᵔᵔ

Most children love carrots. Carrots are rich in vitamin A, necessary to keep cell membranes strong and resistant to infections. Vitamin A does more than promote good eyesight!

1 teaspoon vegetable oil
1½ cups peeled, sliced carrots
¼ cup peeled, diced turnip
¼ cup sliced leek or green onions
2 cups chicken broth
2 tablespoons small enriched pasta
¼ teaspoon ground coriander

Optional: Milk or extra broth to thin soup
Plain low-fat yogurt for garnish

1. In a medium-size saucepan, heat oil. Add vegetables and sauté for 3 minutes.
2. Add broth and pasta. Bring to a boil. Reduce to a simmer and cook until pasta is very tender, 10 to 15 minutes.
3. Remove 4 carrot slices to save for garnish. Pour remaining mixture into food processor or blender and puree.
4. Return soup to saucepan. Add coriander. If desired, thin soup with milk or broth.
5. Serve garnished with yogurt, if desired, and reserved carrots.

Yield: 1½ cups

· Soup in a Shell ·

This soup uses the squash shell as a bowl.

1 acorn squash
2 teaspoons margarine
½ cup milk
⅛ teaspoon nutmeg, if desired
Salt and pepper to taste

1. Preheat oven to 350°. Grease a baking pan with additional margarine or vegetable spray.
2. Cut squash in half horizontally. Remove seeds.
3. Place squash, cut side down, on prepared pan. Bake for 40 minutes.
4. Remove from oven. Cut stem off. Place each squash half in a bowl.
5. Put 1 teaspoon margarine in each squash.
6. With a spoon, scoop, stir, and mash squash, gradually adding ¼ cup milk to each, leaving a thin shell.
7. Season to taste and serve.

Yield: 2 servings

·EGGS·

·Egg Recipes·

Omelet *Fines Herbes*
 Daddy's Jelly Omelet
 Vegetable Omelet
 David's Currant and Pine Nut Omelet
 Blueberry and Spinach Omelet
Egg Roll-ups
Baked Tomato Custard
Kale Timbale
Water-Fried Egg
Sun and Clouds

Eggs are an excellent source of many key nutrients for young children, and they are versatile, economical, and easy to prepare.

Some of our recipes contain one whole egg and one extra egg white to reduce the amount of cholesterol and saturated fat from egg yolks. What do you do with extra yolks? Some people use them as a hair conditioner. Author Jane Brody advises people to give them to the cat or dog. She says yolks make the animals' coats shiny but do not clog their arteries. Another suggestion is to cook and crumble the yolks and add them to the bird feeder.

One word of caution: Food safety experts say eggs should *never* be eaten raw because of the risk of salmonella food poisoning. Do not give your child, or anyone else in your family, homemade egg-type drinks, Caesar salad with raw egg, desserts made with uncooked meringue, or homemade mayonnaise. Young children are especially vulnerable to salmonella. Heat destroys salmonella, if it is present.

· Omelet *Fines Herbes* ·

Omelets are easier for young children to eat with the fingers than scrambled eggs. The basic technique of preparing an omelet remains the same, only the fillings are changed.

1 teaspoon chopped fresh parsley
1 teaspoon chopped fresh basil, or ¼ teaspoon
   dried basil
1 teaspoon chopped fresh chives or green onion
1 egg, or 1 egg plus 1 white
1 tablespoon milk
1 teaspoon margarine

1. In a small bowl, combine herbs.
2. In a medium-size bowl, beat egg with milk.

3. In a small skillet or omelet pan, melt margarine over medium-high heat.
4. Add egg mixture and cook for 30 seconds. Slip a spatula under egg mixture, tilting pan, allowing any uncooked egg to flow under cooked portion.
5. Spoon herbs down center of omelet.
6. With a spatula, loosen one side of omelet and fold it one-third over the remainder. Loosen folded portion and fold over again, in the same direction. Slide onto a plate.

Yield: 1 serving

Daddy's Jelly Omelet

1 egg, or 1 egg plus 1 white
1 tablespoon milk
1 teaspoon margarine
1 teaspoon jelly or jam

1. Proceed as in steps 2 through 4 of Omelet *Fines Herbes*, spooning jelly onto omelet in step 5. Then proceed with step 6.

Yield: 1 serving

Vegetable Omelet

1 egg, or 1 egg plus 1 white
1 tablespoon milk
1 teaspoon margarine
1 tablespoon chopped cooked vegetables (broccoli,
    carrots, peas, spinach)

1. Proceed as in steps 2 through 4 of Omelet *Fines Herbes*, spooning vegetables onto omelet in step 5. Then proceed with step 6.

Yield: 1 serving

David's Currant and Pine Nut Omelet

Do not give this to children under age three, as currants and nuts can cause choking.

> 1 egg, or 1 egg plus 1 white
> 1 tablespoon milk
> 1 teaspoon margarine
> ½ teaspoon pine nuts or chopped walnuts
> 1 teaspoon currants or raisins
> 1 tablespoon grated Swiss cheese

1. Proceed as in steps 2 through 4 of Omelet *Fines Herbes*, spooning nuts, currants, and cheese onto omelet in step 5. Then proceed with step 6.

Yield: 1 serving

Blueberry and Spinach Omelet

> 1½ teaspoons margarine
> 1 tablespoon fresh or frozen blueberries
> 1 teaspoon chopped fresh spinach
> 1 egg, or 1 egg plus 1 white
> 1 tablespoon milk

1. In a small skillet or omelet pan, melt 1 teaspoon margarine over medium-high heat.
2. Add blueberries and spinach. Sauté over medium-high heat until softened, 1 to 2 minutes.
3. In a medium-size bowl, beat egg with milk.
4. Add ½ teaspoon margarine to pan.
5. Pour egg over blueberry mixture and proceed as in steps 2 through 4 of Omelet *Fines Herbes*. Omit step 5 and continue with step 6.

Yield: 1 serving

· Egg Roll-ups ·

You can add chopped tomatoes, avocados, or other vegetables for a change or substitute a slice of whole-grain bread flattened with a rolling pin for the tortilla.

1 flour tortilla
1 egg
1 tablespoon milk
1 teaspoon margarine
2 tablespoons shredded cheese (Monterey Jack, mozzarella, cheddar)

1. Heat tortilla according to package directions.
2. In a small bowl, beat egg with milk.
3. In a small skillet, heat margarine over medium-high heat.
4. Pour egg into skillet and scramble.
5. Spoon egg along one side of tortilla. Sprinkle with cheese. Roll up.

Yield: 1 roll

· Baked Tomato Custard ·

These can be served warm or chilled, as an entrée or snack.

2 teaspoons margarine
4 eggs
1/4 cup milk
2 1/2 tablespoons chopped tomato
2 teaspoons tomato paste
1/2 teaspoon dried basil
1/4 cup grated mozzarella cheese

1. Preheat oven to 350°. Grease 4 small ovenproof custard cups with margarine.
2. In a medium-size bowl, beat eggs with milk. Set aside.
3. In a small bowl, mix tomato, tomato paste, and basil.
4. Place tomato mixture in bottoms of custard cups. Pour in egg mixture.
5. Sprinkle mozzarella on top.
6. Place custard cups in a deep pan. Put into oven. Pour boiling water into pan halfway up the sides of the custard cups.
7. Bake for about 20 minutes, or until a knife inserted in the center comes out clean.

Yield: 4 custards

· Kale Timbale ·

᠅᠅᠅᠅᠅᠅᠅᠅᠅᠅᠅᠅᠅᠅᠅᠅᠅᠅᠅᠅᠅᠅᠅᠅

These are good served warm with tomato sauce or as a cold snack with crackers. You may substitute spinach for the kale.

2 teaspoons margarine
1/4 cup chopped, cooked kale
2 eggs
1/2 cup evaporated milk
1/8 teaspoon ground nutmeg

1. Preheat oven to 325°. Grease 12 mini-muffin cups with margarine.
2. Place 1 teaspoon kale in each muffin cup.
3. In a small bowl, beat eggs. Add milk and nutmeg, and beat well.
4. Spoon 2 tablespoons egg mixture into each muffin cup.
5. Bake for 20 minutes. Unmold and serve, or chill and serve later.

Yield: 12 timbales

·Water-Fried Egg·

Serve with Cheese Crouton Strips (see page 101).

2 tablespoons water or broth
2 teaspoons chopped tomato or sweet red pepper
1 egg
¼ teaspoon chopped fresh basil or parsley, if
    desired
1 teaspoon grated cheese

1. In a small skillet, heat liquid to boiling.
2. Add vegetable, then egg. Reduce to simmer and cook for 2
   minutes.
3. Sprinkle with basil or parsley, if desired, and cheese.
4. Cover and cook until yolk is partially set, about 4 minutes. Remove cover after 2 minutes to check.
5. Transfer egg to a plate and top with remaining liquid.

Yield: 1 serving

· Sun and Clouds ·

What a pretty egg, especially when it's served on a sky-blue plate!

1 teaspoon margarine
1 slice whole-grain bread, lightly toasted
1 egg
2 tablespoons grated cheddar cheese

1. Preheat oven to 400°. Grease a small baking sheet with ½ tea-spoon margarine.
2. Spread remaining ½ teaspoon margarine on toast. Cut toast into a circle, about 3½ inches in diameter. Place toast on baking sheet.
3. Separate egg yolk from white. Place white into a small mixing bowl and yolk into another small bowl.
4. Beat white until stiff. Fold in cheese, reserving 1 teaspoon.
5. Spread egg white on toast and make a small indentation in the center.
6. Carefully slide yolk into the center. Sprinkle with reserved cheese.
7. Bake for 10 minutes, until yolk is set and white is golden.

Yield: 1 serving

·CHEESE·

· Cheese Recipes ·

Summer BMT—Basil, Mozzarella, Tomatoes
Cheese "Blintzes"
Cheese Crouton Strips
Cheese Thimbles
Savory Cheese Mini-tarts
Cookie Cutter Cheeses
Goat Cheese Dip or Spread

C heese is a great source of protein and calcium for young children. Very-high-fat cheeses, such as Brie and cream cheese, have relatively little protein and calcium.

When cheese is combined with "incomplete" vegetable protein foods, such as dried beans or peas or even macaroni, the protein in both foods can be used to build new cells and tissues.

Children can practice their cutting skills with a table knife and a slice of soft cheese. Let them use cookie cutters to cut shapes out of sliced cheese.

· Summer BMT—Basil, · Mozzarella, Tomatoes

The following dish is especially good in the middle of summer when tomatoes are fresh and flavorful, right off the vine.

$1/2$ cup diced mozzarella cheese
1 cup diced fresh tomato
$1/2$ cup fresh basil leaves, finely chopped
4 teaspoons olive oil
8 $1/4$-inch slices Italian-style baguette ($1^1/2$- to 2-inch diameter)

1. Place 2 tablespoons cheese in the center of each plate.
2. Arrange $1/4$ cup tomatoes around cheese.
3. Sprinkle $1/2$ teaspoon basil on top of tomatoes and cheese.
4. Drizzle 2 teaspoons oil over tomatoes and cheese.
5. Brush bread slices with remaining 2 teaspoons oil and toast lightly in a toaster oven or broiler. Arrange 2 slices on each plate.

Yield: 4 servings

·Cheese "Blintzes"·

This is an easy luncheon dish or snack, or try serving them for breakfast.

1 slice whole-grain bread, crusts removed, flattened
   with a rolling pin
$1/2$ teaspoon apple butter or jam
1 tablespoon small-curd cottage cheese
1 teaspoon grated apple or other finely chopped
   fruit
$1/2$ teaspoon margarine, melted
$1/8$ teaspoon sugar
$1/8$ teaspoon cinnamon

1. Place bread on plate and spread with apple butter or jam.
2. In a small bowl, mix cheese and fruit. Spoon mixture along one
   end of bread. Roll up bread, jelly-roll fashion.
3. Brush top with melted margarine.
4. In a small bowl, mix sugar and cinnamon.
5. Sprinkle blintz with sugar-cinnamon mixture.
6. Place blintz in toaster oven or under broiler and toast lightly.

Yield: 1 serving

· Cheese Crouton Strips ·

These strips are easy to hold and make good "take-along" food. They make a good snack, with fresh fruit. Store strips in an airtight container or freeze them and reheat in a 450° oven for 5 minutes.

2 tablespoons vegetable oil
4 slices whole-grain or black bread, crusts removed
$\frac{1}{2}$ cup grated Parmesan cheese

1. Preheat oven to 275°. Grease a cookie sheet with some of the oil or with vegetable spray.
2. Brush a small amount of oil onto each side of bread.
3. Cut each slice of bread into 4 strips. Cut strips in half.
4. In a shallow dish, place cheese. Roll strips in cheese. Place on prepared cookie sheet.
5. Bake 45 minutes or until hard and crunchy.

Yield: 24 to 32 strips

· Cheese Thimbles ·

When the sticky cheese is rolled in currants and refrigerated, it is quite easy to pick up and eat as a finger food. The combination of the tangy cottage cheese and sweet currants makes a nice play group or party treat for children over three.

> ½ cup cottage cheese
> ½ cup dried currants or finely chopped dried
> apricots

1. In a blender or food processor, puree cheese.
2. Line a small sieve with a coffee filter; place sieve over a cup or bowl, spoon cheese into filter, cover with plastic wrap, and refrigerate several hours or overnight.
3. Remove cheese from refrigerator and discard liquid. Form cheese into walnut-size balls (they will be a little sticky).
4. Roll balls in currants and place on a serving plate.
5. Refrigerate for several hours.

Yield: 8 to 12 thimbles

· Savory Cheese Mini-tarts ·

Children like these little bone builders, which have an interesting shape and texture. Evaporated milk is a great ingredient for foods for young children. When water is removed, the remaining milk is twice as concentrated in all nutrients. When portions and appetites are small, nutrient-packed ingredients are especially important.

1 teaspoon vegetable oil
2 to 4 slices whole-grain bread, crusts removed
$\frac{1}{2}$ cup shredded cheese (Swiss or mozzarella)
4 teaspoons finely chopped raw or cooked carrots or
   other vegetables
1 egg
$\frac{1}{2}$ cup evaporated milk
$\frac{1}{8}$ teaspoon ground cinnamon or nutmeg

1. Preheat oven to 400°. Brush 4 mini-muffin cups with $\frac{1}{2}$ teaspoon oil.
2. Roll each bread slice as thin as possible. Cut into circles with a $2\frac{1}{2}$-inch round cookie cutter (or cut each slice in half diagonally) and fit into muffin cups so that the bread comes up the sides of the cups.
3. Brush bread with remaining $\frac{1}{2}$ teaspoon oil, adding a little more if necessary.
4. In each bread-lined muffin cup, place 1 tablespoon cheese and 1 teaspoon carrots or other vegetables.
5. In a small bowl, beat egg with milk and cinnamon or nutmeg. Spoon over cheese and carrot mixture.
6. Sprinkle remaining cheese on tops.
7. Bake for 10 to 15 minutes, until lightly browned and puffy.

Yield: 4 tarts

·Cookie Cutter Cheeses·

Reduced-fat versions of many types of cheese are now available. Cheeses are perfect for holiday parties, accompanied by bread, cut in companion shapes (pumpkin cheese and black cat bread). Older children will have fun preparing this dish. Let them eat the cheese scraps. Extra minerals here, extra minerals there. . . .

1 to 2 ounces sliced cheese per child (Monterey
   Jack, brick, Muenster, cheddar, Swiss)
All shapes and sizes of cookie cutters

1. On a cutting board, place a pile of cheese slices.
2. Using your cookie cutter, cut shapes (pumpkins and moons at Halloween, Santa and stars at Christmas, hearts at Valentine's Day, etc.)
3. Arrange on a serving platter with bread or crackers.

· Goat Cheese Dip or Spread ·

This is great with lightly steamed or raw vegetables, breadsticks, or spread on toasted French bread.

4 ounces mild, soft goat cheese
3 tablespoons plain low-fat yogurt
1 teaspoon herb seasoning or more to taste

1. In a small bowl, mash cheese with a fork.
2. Add yogurt and stir.
3. Season to taste. Serve immediately or refrigerate.

Yield: $^1/_2$ *cup*

·SALADS·

· Salad Recipes ·

Orange and Green Salad
Steamed Green Salad
Swiss Salad
Roasted Beets in Orange Dressing
Dilled Carrot Salad
Marinated Mushrooms
Country-Style Cauliflower Salad
Creamy Cole Slaw
Confetti Corn Salad
New Potatoes Vinaigrette
Lentil Salad
Chick-Pea Salad
Cracked Wheat Garden
Brown Rice Salad with Peas
Minted Strawberries
Apricot and Cherry Salad
Curried Peaches
Summer Melon Salad
Winter Fruit Salad

A salad is not, by definition, "nutritious." Vegetables that are soaked in water or fruits that are cut up hours before serving quickly depreciate in vitamin strength. And a youngster who goes to the salad bar and fills his or her bowl with nothing but croutons and bacon bits should not be praised for eating salad!

The recipes in this section contain a variety of fruits, vegetables, pasta, and beans, put together in tasty and colorful combinations. If your child is a reluctant salad eater, try a do-it-yourself salad of bite-size fruits and blanched or raw vegetables with a little container of dressing or dip.

Raw fresh fruits and vegetables are a better source of vitamin C than cooked fruits and vegetables. Fruits and vegetables provide nature's very best chewable vitamins for your child every day.

·Orange and Green Salad·

If your preschooler prefers, arrange the oranges, greens, and sprouts on a plate with a small bowl of dressing for dipping (double the recipe).

> 1 cup seedless orange segments, halved, or
> drained, canned mandarin oranges
> 1 cup salad greens (lettuce, spinach, arugula,
> mache)
> 1/4 cup orange juice
> 1 teaspoon sherry vinegar
> 4 teaspoons walnut oil
> 4 teaspoons plain low-fat yogurt
> 1/2 teaspoon sugar
> 4 teaspoons sunflower or other sprouts

1. In a serving bowl, combine orange segments and salad greens.
2. In a small bowl, combine juice, vinegar, oil, yogurt, and sugar. Pour over salad. Toss.
3. Sprinkle with sprouts.

Yield: 4 servings

· Steamed Green Salad ·

Very fresh beet or other greens are rich in iron and vitamin A. They have a nutty flavor when steamed. If you can't find fresh beet greens, substitute spinach, kale, or Swiss chard. This salad is good with hard-cooked eggs and Cheese Crouton Strips (see page 101).

4 cups roughly chopped, well-cleaned, very fresh
   beet greens, stems removed
2 tablespoons water
2 teaspoons olive oil
¼ teaspoon lemon juice

1. In a large deep skillet, place greens and water. Cook, covered, over medium heat for 5 minutes.
2. Remove cover and continue cooking, if necessary, until water is evaporated.
3. In a medium-size bowl, combine greens, oil, and lemon juice. Refrigerate until cold, up to two days.

Yield: 1 cup

· Swiss Salad ·

This is a nice, simple lunch that can be prepared ahead and served with whole-grain toast or crackers and a glass of cold juice or milk. It can also be used as a filling for crêpes or as a topping for a waffle.

1/3 cup grated Swiss cheese
1/4 cup cooked green beans, cut into 1/2-inch pieces
1 teaspoon olive oil
1/4 teaspoon lemon juice

1. In a small bowl, mix all ingredients. Stir to combine.
2. Refrigerate for at least 1 hour to blend flavors.

Yield: 1/2 cup

· Roasted Beets in Orange ·
Dressing

Try this cold, colorful beet salad. In this recipe, the orange flavor enhances the sweetness of the beets. Although it is a good finger food, remember that beets stain, so have the bibs and napkins handy.

5 medium beets (2 inches in diameter), unpeeled,
   greens and stems removed
3 tablespoons vegetable oil
¼ cup sliced orange segments
½ teaspoon cider vinegar
2 tablespoons orange juice

1. Preheat oven to 450°.
2. Scrub and dry beets. Place in a baking pan.
3. Drizzle 2 tablespoons oil over beets.
4. Roast for 1 hour or until tender.
5. Remove from oven and, as soon as you can handle them, peel the beets and slice into wedges or dice.
6. In a medium-size bowl, mix beets and orange segments.
7. Pour vinegar, orange juice, and remaining 1 tablespoon oil over beets and toss lightly.
8. Refrigerate to allow flavors to blend.

Yield: 1³/₄ cups

· Dilled Carrot Salad ·

We discovered the real value of this salad while waiting impatiently at our neighborhood gourmet take-out store. Because lunchtime was near and the line was long, the thoughtful salesperson offered the children a dish of carrot salad to snack on. This adapted version bears testimony to its success. Choose carrots that are thin or small. Large, thick carrots are not as sweet or tasty. Also, carrots with a deeper orange color have more vitamin A.

6 carrots, peeled and cut in 1-inch-long, ⅛-inch-
    wide julienne strips (about 1½ cups)
2 green onions, chopped
4 teaspoons dried dill, or 2 tablespoons chopped
    fresh dill
2 teaspoons cider vinegar
2 tablespoons olive oil
1 teaspoon ground dried ginger
1 teaspoon maple syrup or honey
Salt and pepper to taste

1. In a medium-size bowl, combine carrots, green onion, and dill.
2. In a small bowl, mix vinegar, oil, ginger, and maple syrup.
3. Pour vinegar and oil mixture over carrots. Season to taste.
4. Chill for several hours or overnight.

Yield: 2 cups

· Marinated Mushrooms ·

This lovely salad is from Al Mercante, a restaurant in Milan. This simple adaptation makes a nice salad or snack. Mushrooms are a secret source of many trace minerals—magnesium, copper, and selenium.

2 teaspoons lemon juice
2 tablespoons olive oil
¼ teaspoon dried tarragon, or 2 teaspoons chopped
   fresh tarragon
Pinch of sugar, if desired
6 large, white mushrooms, wiped clean and sliced
   very thin
3 tablespoons shredded Parmesan, Asiago, or
   provolone cheese
2 teaspoons chopped fresh parsley or chervil

1. In a medium-size bowl, combine lemon juice, oil, and tarragon, and sugar, if desired.
2. Add mushrooms and toss. Refrigerate in a small covered container or plastic bag for several hours to blend flavors.
3. To serve, spoon some mushrooms into a bowl. Sprinkle with cheese and parsley.

Yield: 1 cup

· Country-Style ·
Cauliflower Salad

This salad was inspired by a family-operated restaurant in the hills high above Eze, in the south of France. The white, red, and green vegetables are very colorful.

1 cup cauliflower pieces, broken into very tiny
   flowerets
1/2 cup peeled, diced carrot
1 small green onion, finely chopped
1/2 cup diced sweet red pepper or tomato
1/4 cup plain low-fat yogurt
1 teaspoon Dijon mustard
1 teaspoon lemon juice
1 teaspoon fresh chopped parsley

1. In a medium-size pot, bring water to a boil. Add cauliflower and carrot. Continue boiling for 2 minutes, until tender but still crisp. Run under cold water and drain well.
2. In a medium-size bowl, mix cauliflower, carrot, green onion, and pepper or tomato.
3. In a small bowl, mix yogurt, mustard, lemon juice, and parsley. Pour over vegetables. Stir until well coated.
4. Chill for several hours or overnight to blend flavors.

Yield: 1³/₄ cups

· Creamy Cole Slaw ·

ᘉᘉᘉᘉᘉᘉᘉᘉᘉᘉᘉᘉᘉᘉᘉᘉᘉᘉᘉᘉᘉᘉᘉᘉᘉᘉᘉᘉᘉᘉ

Cabbage is a good source of vitamin C, but the vitamin is easily destroyed, particularly when the cabbage is cut and exposed to air. In order to retain the maximum nutritional value of this dish, cover the slaw tightly with plastic wrap before refrigerating it.

½ pound green cabbage, cored (2 cups shredded)
1 large carrot, peeled
½ large apple, peeled, halved, and cored
¼ medium sweet onion
2 tablespoons mayonnaise
¼ cup plain low-fat yogurt
1 teaspoon cider vinegar
1 teaspoon sugar
1 teaspoon Dijon mustard

1. In a food processor, shred cabbage, carrot, apple, and onion. Place in a medium-size mixing bowl.
2. Add mayonnaise, yogurt, vinegar, sugar, and mustard to the cabbage mixture. Stir to combine.
3. Cover and refrigerate for several hours or overnight.

Yield: 4 cups

· Confetti Corn Salad ·

Corn is the favorite vegetable of many children. It is a valuable source of dietary fiber. This colorful salad keeps several days and is a great sandwich filling, mixed with tuna fish. Serve on romaine or spinach leaves, in a tomato shell, or in a pita bread.

2 cups cooked corn kernels, fresh or frozen
$1/3$ cup finely diced sweet red pepper
$1/3$ cup finely diced sweet green pepper
2 tablespoons chopped fresh parsley
1 tablespoon lemon juice
1 small shallot or green onion, minced
$1/2$ teaspoon Dijon mustard
3 tablespoons vegetable oil

Optional: $1/4$ teaspoon ground coriander
$1/2$ teaspoon dried sage, crumbled

1. In a medium-size bowl, mix corn, peppers, and parsley.
2. In a small bowl, mix remaining ingredients, including coriander and sage, if desired, to form vinaigrette.
3. Toss corn mixture with vinaigrette.
4. Refrigerate for several hours or overnight to blend flavors.

Yield: $2^{1}/_{2}$ cups

· New Potatoes Vinaigrette ·

Small new potatoes are a richer source of vitamin C than larger potatoes. This is particularly delicious made with warm potatoes, which absorb more seasoning flavor than cold potatoes. Olive oil is a monounsaturated oil that is good for the heart.

4 small, cooked new red potatoes, unpeeled
1/2 teaspoon lemon juice
1/4 teaspoon Dijon mustard
1/4 teaspoon chopped fresh parsley
1/4 teaspoon snipped fresh chives, or 1/8 teaspoon
   dried chives
1 tablespoon olive oil

1. Dice potatoes. Place in a medium-size bowl.
2. In a small bowl, mix lemon juice, mustard, parsley, and chives. Whisk in oil to form vinaigrette.
3. Pour vinaigrette over potatoes. Toss. Serve immediately.

Yield: About 1 cup

· Lentil Salad ·

Packed into little plastic cups with lids, this makes a nice protein dish for picnics or carry-along meals. Serve with bread and cheese for a complete meal.

½ cup dry lentils, rinsed
2 cloves garlic, unpeeled
1 bay leaf
1 green onion, chopped
½ cup chopped sweet red pepper
1 teaspoon white or red wine vinegar
½ teaspoon Dijon mustard
3 tablespoons olive oil
¼ cup finely chopped fresh parsley
Salt and pepper to taste

1. In a small saucepan, combine lentils, garlic, and bay leaf. Cover with water 1 inch above lentils. Bring to a boil. Reduce to a simmer and cook until tender, 10 to 20 minutes. Drain.
2. Discard garlic and bay leaf.
3. In a medium-size bowl, mix lentils, green onion, and red pepper.
4. In a small bowl, whisk together vinegar, mustard, and oil to form vinaigrette.
5. Stir vinaigrette and parsley into lentils. Season to taste.
6. Refrigerate for several hours to blend flavors.

Yield: 2 cups

· Chick-Pea Salad ·

Chick-peas are a good source of vegetable protein and fiber. Serve the salad on romaine lettuce leaves or inside pita bread pockets. Toddlers like to pick up chick-peas with their fingers. But watch children carefully so they don't choke. For younger children, you can puree the whole salad in a food processor and make a chick-pea spread.

1 cup canned, drained chick-peas
3 tablespoons diced sweet green pepper
2 tablespoons peeled, seeded, and diced cucumber
$1/2$ tablespoon chopped fresh parsley
$1/2$ cup diced tomato
3 tablespoons plain low-fat yogurt
2 teaspoons snipped fresh dill weed, or $1/4$ teaspoon
  dried dill
$1/2$ teaspoon lemon juice
1 tablespoon vegetable oil
Salt and pepper to taste

1. In a medium-size bowl, combine all ingredients.
2. Refrigerate for several hours to allow flavors to blend.

Yield: 2 cups

· Cracked Wheat Garden ·

This is fun to make in summer with herbs and vegetables from the garden. If you add beans, lentils, peas, tuna, chicken, or cheese, this becomes a hearty protein dish, especially if it is served with plain or lemon yogurt as a topping.

1 cup medium-fine bulgur (cracked wheat)
1½ cups water
1 cup peeled, seeded, and finely diced cucumber
1 cup finely diced tomato
2 green onions, chopped
2 tablespoons chopped fresh basil or mint leaves
¼ cup chopped fresh parsley
⅛ teaspoon salt
Dash of freshly ground pepper
3 tablespoons lemon juice
2 tablespoons olive oil
1 clove garlic, peeled and minced

1. Soak bulgur in the water for 1 hour, until wheat is light and fluffy but not mushy. Drain well. Shake in large strainer, pressing with hands to remove all water.
2. In a medium-size bowl, mix bulgur, vegetables, herbs, salt, and pepper.
3. In a small bowl, mix lemon juice, oil, and garlic as dressing.
4. Pour dressing over bulgur mixture and toss.
5. Refrigerate for several hours or overnight to blend flavors.

Yield: 4½ cups

· Brown Rice Salad with Peas ·

A nice accompaniment with roast meat or poultry.

1/2 cup uncooked brown rice
4 cups water
1/2 cup frozen peas
1/4 cup peeled and finely diced carrot
1 chopped green onion, if desired
3 tablespoons olive oil
1 teaspoon red wine vinegar
1/2 teaspoon Dijon mustard
Salt and pepper to taste

1. In a medium-size saucepan, heat rice and water to boiling. Reduce to a simmer and cook, covered, for 15 minutes, or until done.
2. Drain rice. Pour into a medium-size bowl while still warm.
3. Add peas and carrot, and onion, if desired. Stir to mix.
4. In a small bowl, mix oil, vinegar, and mustard. Season to taste.
5. Add oil mixture to rice mixture. Stir well.
6. Refrigerate for several hours or overnight. Bring to room temperature before serving.

Yield: About 2 1/2 cups

· Minted Strawberries ·

Best in spring or summer when strawberries are at their peak. Serve with Jelled Orange Cream (see page 290).

1 cup sliced strawberries
1½ teaspoons undiluted orange juice concentrate
1 teaspoon chopped fresh mint leaves
Whole mint leaves for garnish

1. In a medium-size bowl, mix strawberries, orange juice concentrate, and chopped mint leaves. Refrigerate for several hours.
2. Garnish with whole mint leaves and serve chilled.

Yield: 1 cup

· Apricot and Cherry Salad ·

Fresh apricots and cherries last for such a short time! This early-summer salad is a good way to take advantage of their bright colors, sweet taste, and vitamins.

1 tablespoon vanilla yogurt
¼ teaspoon almond extract
1 apricot, pitted and diced
4 cherries, pitted and quartered

1. In a small bowl, mix yogurt and almond extract.
2. Add apricots and cherries. Toss gently.

Yield: 1 serving

· Summer Melon Salad ·

This is a nice side dish with cold Rolled Turkey Breast (see page 199).

$^{1}/_{2}$ medium cantaloupe, cut into balls
$^{1}/_{2}$ medium honeydew, cut into balls
1 teaspoon vanilla

Optional: 2 sprigs fresh thyme

1. In a medium-size bowl, combine cantaloupe, honeydew, and vanilla. Stir to mix.
2. If desired for flavor, push thyme into center of melon balls.
3. Cover with plastic wrap and refrigerate for 2 or more hours.
4. Remove thyme before serving.

Yield: 2 cups

·Winter Fruit Salad·

A crisp, savory fruit salad.

1 firm, ripe Bosc pear, peeled, cored, and diced
½ apple, peeled, cored, and diced
1 orange, peeled, segmented, and cut into bite-size
  pieces
¼ cup (10 to 12) red seedless grapes, quartered
1 tablespoon olive oil
1 teaspoon balsamic vinegar
2 sprigs fresh rosemary

1. In a medium-size bowl, mix all ingredients.
2. Refrigerate for several hours. Before serving, remove rosemary
   and toss fruit gently.

Yield: About 2 cups

·Curried Peaches·

∿∿∿∿∿∿∿∿∿∿∿∿∿∿∿∿∿∿∿∿∿∿∿∿∿∿

Some children resist vegetables. Savory fruit makes a good alternative accompaniment to poultry, meat, and fish.

8 peach slices (fresh or canned in juice)
1/8 teaspoon curry powder

1. Preheat broiler or toaster oven.
2. Place peach slices on broiling pan. Sprinkle with curry powder.
3. Broil for a few minutes until peaches begin to brown. Serve warm.

Yield: 8 slices

·VEGETABLES·

· Vegetable Recipes ·

Glazed Yellow Squash, Leeks, and Carrots with Chives
Orange Spiced Carrot Coins
Brussels Sprouts on a Stick
Cauliflower in Cheese "Sauce"
Broccoli and Onions
Gingered Broccoli
Stuffed Zucchini Cups
Baked Zucchini Parmesan
Spaghetti Squash with Asparagus
Autumn Squash Compote
Sweet and Sour Red Cabbage
Spinach Fingers
Italian Greens
Kale with Red Pepper
Mediterranean Collards
"Tempura"-Style Vegetables
Snow Pea Pod Stir-Fry
Baby Lima Beans
Braised Chestnuts
Pureed Parsnips and Cauliflower
Apple and Leek Sauté
Eggplant Melts
Carrot-Potato-Leek Pancakes
Crispy Potato Fingers
Creamed Potatoes
Sweet Potatoes
Sweet Potato Circles

L et your child select vegetables at the supermarket or vegetable stand and help prepare them. If children are in on the selection process, they're more likely to be interested in eating vegetables. Some children like their vegetables hot; some like them cold; some like them crisp; others like them soft. Many like raw vegetables.

Always peel vegetables you give to young children. Kids have a lower tolerance level of pesticide residues than adults.

To maximize vegetable vitamin retention:

- Store vegetables in the refrigerator in airtight containers.
- Don't soak cut vegetables in water.
- Cut vegetables shortly before serving when possible.
- Steam or cook vegetables in minimal amounts of water.

· Glazed Yellow Squash, Leeks, · and Carrots with Chives

This colorful dish has a wonderful flavor from the reduced broth and goes well with simply prepared meats, in a crêpe, or in an omelet.

1 medium yellow summer squash, ends removed,
    sliced in 1/4-inch circles
1 leek, white only, julienned
1 medium carrot, peeled and julienned
1 teaspoon dried chives, or 2 teaspoons snipped
    fresh chives
1/2 teaspoon dried chervil or parsley, or 2 teaspoons
    chopped fresh parsley
3/4 cup fish or chicken broth

1. In a small saucepan, mix squash, leek, carrot, chives, and chervil or parsley.
2. Add broth and bring to a boil. Cook over high heat for about 20 minutes, until broth is reduced and the vegetables are glazed.

Yield: 1 1/2 cups

· Orange Spiced Carrot Coins ·

Almost every child loves carrots, raw or cooked. They are also an excellent source of vitamin A.

1/2 pound (4 to 5) young, tender carrots, peeled and
   sliced into 1/4-inch circles
1/4 cup water
1/4 cup orange juice
1 1/2 teaspoons margarine
1/4 teaspoon vanilla
1/8 teaspoon ground nutmeg

1. In a medium-size saucepan, combine carrots, water, orange juice, and margarine. Cover pan tightly and simmer over low heat until carrots are crisp-tender, about 20 minutes. Check to make sure water does not evaporate; add a few tablespoons of water, if necessary.
2. When carrots are cooked, remove from heat and add vanilla and nutmeg. Mix well.

Yield: 2 cups

· Brussels Sprouts on a Stick ·

I steam Brussels sprouts in the morning to serve cold at dinner and reserve a couple for an afternoon snack. Michael loves this cute treat.

2 fresh Brussels sprouts (cooked in boiling water for
    10 minutes), or 2 frozen Brussels sprouts, thawed
4 skinny pretzel sticks
1 mini-bagel
1 teaspoon ketchup, Aioli Sauce (p. 226), or Golden
    Dippy Sauce (p. 225)

1. Cut each sprout in half lengthwise.
2. With a sharp knife, poke a hole in bottom end of each half sprout. Carefully push pretzel into hole.
3. Place whole bagel on plate. Stick pretzel into bagel with sprout in the air. (It will look like a little tree.) Repeat with remaining 3 pieces.
4. Serve immediately, with dipping sauce.

Yield: 1 serving (4 pieces)

· Cauliflower in Cheese "Sauce" ·

This was created in haste but remains Michael's favorite side dish or snack. Try substituting blanched or steamed broccoli or Brussels sprouts for the cauliflower. It's a nutritious finger food.

4 bite-size pieces blanched or steamed cauliflower
4 small pieces mild cheddar cheese (about ½
    ounce or ½ slice total)

1. On a piece of aluminum foil, place cauliflower pieces.
2. Put a piece of cheese on each piece of cauliflower.
3. Toast lightly in toaster oven or place in broiler to melt. Serve warm or at room temperature.

Yield: 1 serving

· Broccoli and Onions ·

Broccoli is one of the most nutritious vegetables, and children love the "little trees."

1 tablespoon olive oil
½ cup finely chopped sweet onion (Spanish, red, or
    Vidalia)
2 cups broccoli flowerets

1. In a heavy skillet or wok, heat oil.
2. Add onion and broccoli. Stir-fry over high heat until lightly browned, about 3 minutes.
3. Reduce heat to low. Cover. Cook for 5 minutes, until flowerets are tender.

Yield: 1¹/₂ cups

· Gingered Broccoli ·

This bright-green broccoli with its piquant ginger glaze goes well with roast chicken or turkey.

3 cups broccoli flowerets
3 tablespoons chicken broth
1 clove garlic, peeled and minced
¹/₂ teaspoon grated, peeled fresh gingerroot
1¹/₂ tablespoons reduced-sodium soy sauce
1¹/₂ teaspoons brown sugar, packed
1 teaspoon sesame oil
1¹/₂ teaspoons cornstarch
1 tablespoon cold water

1. Place broccoli in a large pot of boiling water. Return to boil and cook for 2 minutes. Drain.
2. In a wok or skillet, warm broth over medium-high heat.
3. Add garlic and ginger. Cook, stirring, for 1 minute.
4. Add soy sauce, sugar, and sesame oil.
5. In a small bowl, combine cornstarch and cold water. Add to wok. Cook over medium-high heat, stirring, until sauce thickens, about 1 minute.
6. Stir in broccoli and mix to blend flavors.

Yield: 2¹/₂ cups

· Stuffed Zucchini Cups ·

This is a perfect recipe for summer, when both zucchini and basil are abundant.

2½ teaspoons olive oil
1 medium zucchini
1 tablespoon finely chopped onion
1 teaspoon chopped fresh basil
1 tablespoon shredded mozzarella cheese

1. Preheat oven to 350°. Lightly grease a small baking dish with ½ teaspoon olive oil (or vegetable spray).
2. Remove and discard ends of zucchini. Cut zucchini crosswise into 4 chunks.
3. In a small saucepan, bring 1 inch of water to a boil. Add zucchini and blanch for 2 minutes, until softened.
4. Scoop out zucchini centers, leaving a "shell" ⅛ to ¼ inch thick.
5. In a small skillet, heat remaining 2 teaspoons oil. Add zucchini centers, onion, and basil. Cook over medium heat for 3 minutes, until softened.
6. Place zucchini "shells" on small baking dish. Fill each "shell" with zucchini-onion mixture.
7. Top with cheese.
8. Bake for 10 to 15 minutes, until cheese melts.

Yield: 4 pieces

· Baked Zucchini Parmesan ·

All the Stones love these zucchini boats!

2 tablespoons water
1 teaspoon lemon juice
1 medium zucchini, halved lengthwise and then
    cut in half crosswise, or 2 miniature zucchini,
    halved lengthwise
1 teaspoon Parmesan cheese
1/2 teaspoon margarine

1. Preheat oven to 350°.
2. Mix water and lemon juice in a small baking dish.
3. Place zucchini in dish. Sprinkle with cheese, dot with margarine,
   and bake until tender, about 25 minutes.

Yield: 4 pieces

· Spaghetti Squash with · Asparagus

Cook spaghetti squash in a pot of boiling water until tender, about 15 to 20 minutes for a small squash. When cool enough to handle, cut in half lengthwise, remove seeds, and, using a fork, remove the spaghettilike strands. Give your child a fork to assist in the scraping.

1 tablespoon olive oil
1 clove garlic, peeled and minced
½ cup cooked asparagus tips
¾ cup cooked spaghetti squash (1 medium squash)
3 tablespoons Parmesan cheese

1. In a skillet, heat oil.
2. Add garlic and cook over medium heat for 1 minute.
3. Add asparagus. Cook 3 minutes.
4. Add spaghetti squash. Stir and cook until heated, about 2 minutes.
5. Sprinkle with Parmesan cheese and serve.

Yield: 1¼ cups

·Autumn Squash Compote·

For the holidays, my family loves this sweet dish with roast capon. It freezes well.

1 butternut squash (2½ pounds)
2 Red or Golden Delicious apples
½ cup chopped prunes
2 tablespoons orange juice
¼ cup apple cider
1½ tablespoons brown sugar, packed
1½ tablespoons margarine

1. Preheat oven to 350°.
2. Cut squash in half lengthwise. Remove and discard seeds. Peel and cut into ½-inch chunks.
3. Peel and core apples. Cut into chunks.
4. In a 9-by-12-inch baking pan, mix squash, apples, prunes, orange juice, and cider.
5. Sprinkle sugar over mixture. Dot with margarine.
6. Bake for 30 to 40 minutes, until tender.

Yield: 5 cups

· Sweet and Sour Red Cabbage ·

The American Cancer Society recommends eating cruciferous vegetables, which include those in the cabbage family. Enjoy this sweet and sour dish, which adds a dash of color as well as flavor to dinner plates. It is good served hot or cold with most meats.

1 pound red cabbage (1 small head)
1 tablespoon vegetable oil
1 Granny Smith apple, peeled, cored, and thinly sliced
1 cup grape juice (red or purple)
Salt and pepper to taste
2 teaspoon strawberry jam or jelly
1/2 teaspoon vinegar

1. Preheat oven to 350°.
2. Cut cabbage into quarters and cook in a large pot of boiling water for 5 minutes. Drain thoroughly and chop into shreds with a knife. (There should be about 4 cups shredded cabbage.)
3. Heat oil in a 10-inch oven-proof skillet or 9-by-5-inch flame-proof baking dish.
4. Stir in cabbage and apples; then add grape juice and salt and pepper to taste.
5. Bring liquid to a boil over medium-low heat. Then cover and place in the oven for 35 to 40 minutes.
6. Remove from oven and stir in jam and vinegar. Serve warm or chill and serve as a salad.

Yield: 3 cups

· Spinach Fingers ·

ʊʊʊʊʊʊʊʊʊʊʊʊʊʊʊʊʊʊʊʊʊʊʊʊʊʊʊʊʊʊʊʊ

Spinach Fingers do require a bit more preparation time than most of our recipes, but we think they're worth the extra effort. They can be frozen or refrigerated after step 9.

> 4 cups (¼ pound) fresh spinach leaves, or ½ cup
>   frozen, chopped spinach, defrosted and drained
>   (half a 10-ounce package)
> ⅓ cup dried bread crumbs
> ¼ cup ricotta cheese
> 2 tablespoons Parmesan cheese
> 1 egg
> 1 medium clove garlic, finely minced
> 1½ quarts (6 cups) chicken broth
> 1 tablespoon margarine, melted
> 1 teaspoon dried sage, crumbled
> Freshly grated Parmesan cheese

1. If using frozen spinach, start at step 3. If using fresh spinach, wash thoroughly. Shake to remove excess water. Transfer spinach to a large, deep saucepan. Cover and cook over low heat until wilted, about 5 minutes.
2. Coarsely chop spinach.
3. Drain and squeeze spinach as dry as possible.
4. In a medium-size bowl, combine spinach, bread crumbs, ricotta, Parmesan, egg, and garlic.
5. Using your hands, form into "fingers" ½ by 3 inches. Place on platter or waxed paper until all are made.
6. Preheat oven to 350°. Grease a 9-by-12-inch baking dish with a little margarine.
7. In a medium saucepan, bring broth to a boil.
8. Gently place "fingers" into broth and cook until they float to the top, about 2 minutes.

9. With a slotted spoon, remove "fingers" and place in prepared baking dish. "Fingers" can be refrigerated or frozen at this point.
10. Drizzle melted margarine over "fingers" and sprinkle with sage.
11. Bake for 10 to 15 minutes. Sprinkle with cheese. Serve at room temperature or cold.

Yield: 15 fingers

· Italian Greens ·

Italian greens are an excellent topping for pizza (see page 246) or pasta, as well as a side dish to any roast meat or poultry.

4 cups roughly chopped, well-cleaned beet greens, spinach, or kale
2 tablespoons water
2 teaspoons olive oil
1 clove garlic, peeled and sliced
3 tablespoons grated Parmesan cheese

1. In a large skillet, place greens and water. Cook, covered, over medium heat for 5 minutes.
2. Remove cover and continue cooking, if necessary, until water evaporates.
3. In a medium-size saucepan, heat oil. Add garlic and cook over low heat until garlic begins to brown, about 2 minutes.
4. Remove garlic and stir in cooked greens.
5. Serve with cheese sprinkled on top.

Yield: 1 cup

· Kale with Red Pepper ·

Kale has a distinct taste, especially appealing for a child who likes greens. Try this preparation alone or mixed into pasta, rice, or an omelet.

3/4 pound fresh kale, leaves only (discard stems)
3 tablespoons water
2 tablespoons olive oil
1 sweet red pepper, seeded and diced (about 2/3 cup)
1 clove garlic, peeled and chopped
1 tablespoon olive oil

1. In a large skillet, place kale and water. Cover and cook over medium heat until wilted, about 5 minutes. Remove cover and cook, watching carefully, until water evaporates.
2. Remove kale from skillet and chop coarsely. Reserve.
3. In the same skillet, heat oil. Add red pepper and sauté for 3 minutes. Add garlic and sauté 2 minutes longer.
4. Add kale and oil and sauté 3 minutes longer.
5. Serve warm or at room temperature.

Yield: 1 1/2 cups

·Mediterranean Collards·

The Mediterranean flavors make this an unusual dish.

½ pound frozen, chopped collard greens
1 carrot, peeled and diced
⅔ cup raisins
¼ cup pitted, chopped Calamata or plain olives
½ cup water
1 to 2 tablespoons olive oil
Salt and pepper to taste

1. In a medium-size saucepan, stir collards, carrot, raisins, olives, and water. Simmer for 20 to 25 minutes, until water evaporates.
2. Stir oil into mixture. Season to taste.

NOTE: Leftovers: Puree leftovers and spread on thin slices of French bread. Sprinkle with mozzarella, Parmesan, or provolone cheese. Melt in toaster oven and serve.

Yield: 1½ cups

· "Tempura"-Style Vegetables ·

Traditionally, tempura is made with an assortment of vegetables and/or shrimp, dipped in a light batter and deep-fried. The result is an irresistible, crunchy meal. In our version, vegetables are rolled in batter and baked until crispy and golden. They can be dipped in unsweetened apple butter or melted, unsweetened jelly. Leftovers, if any, can be refrigerated and reheated.

2 tablespoons vegetable oil
1 egg
2 tablespoons milk
1 teaspoon vanilla
$\frac{1}{2}$ cup cornmeal
$\frac{1}{2}$ cup dried bread crumbs
1 tablespoon wheat germ
$\frac{1}{2}$ teaspoon dried thyme
$\frac{1}{2}$ medium acorn squash, peeled and cut into
   $\frac{1}{4}$-inch-thick rings, each ring sliced in half or
   quartered
1 cup fresh mushrooms, cut in half
2 cups zucchini, cut into $\frac{1}{4}$-inch-thick circles

Optional: $\frac{1}{4}$ cup unsweetened apple butter or jelly

1. Preheat oven to 400°. Brush cookie sheet with 2 teaspoons oil (or vegetable spray). Set aside.
2. In a shallow dish, beat egg, milk, and vanilla.
3. In a separate shallow dish, mix cornmeal, bread crumbs, wheat germ, and thyme.
4. Dip vegetables into egg mixture, then into crumb mixture. Place on prepared cookie sheet.
5. Drizzle remaining 4 teaspoons oil over vegetables.
6. Bake for 20 minutes. Turn vegetables over. Bake 10 to 15 minutes longer, until golden brown and crispy.

7. To serve, arrange vegetables on individual plates or on one large plate with apple butter on the side.

Yield: About 5 cups

· Snow Pea Pod Stir-Fry ·

Children love the bright colors and crunchy textures in this vegetable stir-fry.

1 medium carrot, peeled
1 cup snow pea pods
1 tablespoon peanut oil
$^2/_3$ cup sliced fresh mushrooms
1 teaspoon reduced-sodium soy sauce

1. Cut carrot lengthwise, then in cross-cut slices so you have thin half-moon shapes.
2. Cut snow pea pods into $^1/_4$-inch slices.
3. In a medium-size skillet, heat oil.
4. Add carrots and mushrooms. Stir-fry for 1 to 2 minutes.
5. Add snow pea pods. Stir-fry for 1 to 2 minutes, until just tender.
6. Stir in soy sauce.

Yield: 1 cup

· Baby Lima Beans ·

Besides being more tender, baby lima beans have more minerals and fiber than the larger variety. Garlic and thyme add spunk to this often forgotten vegetable.

1/4 cup water
2 cups frozen baby lima beans
1 tablespoon olive oil
1 clove garlic, peeled and minced
1/2 teaspoon dried thyme

1. In a small skillet, bring water to a boil. Add lima beans. Cook over high heat until tender, about 2 minutes.
2. Drain beans in a colander. Dry skillet.
3. In the same skillet, heat oil. Add garlic and thyme. Cook over medium heat for 2 minutes. Add lima beans and cook until heated through.

Yield: 2 cups

· Braised Chestnuts ·

Chestnuts have an appealing, slightly sweet flavor and are soft enough for a young eater to manage. They make an elegant addition to simply roasted poultry dishes. Unsweetened, peeled chestnuts in jars are now available in most supermarkets.

1 cup coarsely chopped, unsweetened chestnuts
1 cup broth, any type
1 small or ½ large bay leaf
Dash of freshly ground pepper

1. In a small saucepan, combine all ingredients.
2. Bring to a boil. Simmer over medium-high heat until sauce is thickened, about 10 minutes.
3. Remove bay leaf before serving.

Yield: 1 cup

·Pureed Parsnips and· Cauliflower

Try this instead of mashed potatoes and serve with roast chicken and steamed asparagus. It's also good with roast pork.

1/2 pound parsnips, peeled and cut into chunks
1/2 pound cauliflower, broken into pieces
3 tablespoons milk
Salt to taste

Optional: 1 tablespoon chopped fresh parsley, basil, mint, or watercress

1. In a medium-size pot of boiling water, place parsnips and cauliflower.
2. Bring water back to a boil and cook for 20 minutes, or until vegetables are softened.
3. Drain well and puree in a food processor, adding milk, until smooth. Add salt.
4. Place in a serving bowl. Sprinkle with parsley, basil, mint, or watercress, if desired.

Yield: 1 1/2 cups

·Apple and Leek Sauté·

This mixture of apples and leeks is nice with grilled meats, spooned onto toast, or rolled in a crêpe or omelet.

½ cup water or broth
1 cup thinly sliced green onion or leek, white part
   only
1 teaspoon margarine
½ cup Golden Delicious apple, peeled, cored, and
   thinly sliced
¼ cup undiluted evaporated milk

1. In a small skillet, heat water or broth to boiling.
2. Add leek or onion and cook over medium-high heat until water is almost evaporated.
3. Add margarine and apple and cook for 2 minutes over medium-high heat, stirring often until lightly browned.
4. Add milk. Continue cooking and stirring for 1 or 2 minutes, until milk is evaporated.
5. Serve warm.

Yield: 1 cup

· Eggplant Melts ·

Let your son or daughter help you choose a shiny, unbruised, firm eggplant. Eggplant tastes wonderful grilled or broiled. A spoonful of chopped tomatoes makes a colorful topping on this recipe.

1 8-inch-long, thin eggplant, skinned, cut in ½-inch slices (if eggplant is not thin, slice it in half lengthwise first)
2 to 3 tablespoons olive oil
½ teaspoon dried basil
½ teaspoon dried thyme
¼ teaspoon garlic powder
1 tablespoon cottage cheese
½ teaspoon grated Parmesan cheese
3 tablespoons chopped tomato

1. Preheat broiler or grill. Grease a baking sheet or grill top.
2. Place eggplant rounds on cookie sheet or plate. Brush with olive oil.
3. Sprinkle herbs and spices on eggplant.
4. Broil or grill for about 5 minutes, until lightly browned (watch carefully). Turn over. Broil or grill for another 5 minutes or until lightly browned and tender when pierced with the point of a knife.
5. Place finished eggplant slices on baking sheet.
6. Spread eggplant with cottage cheese. Sprinkle with Parmesan cheese.
7. Toast or broil until golden.
8. Garnish with chopped tomato.

Yield: 16 pieces

· Carrot-Potato-Leek Pancakes ·

These pancakes are a version of the familiar potato pancake recipe. They are good served with yogurt, sour cream, mild salsa, or applesauce. To freeze, separate cooked pancakes with waxed paper and seal in a freezer bag. Remove as needed and heat in a toaster oven.

1 large baking potato, peeled
1 medium carrot, peeled
1 whole leek, washed and green leaves discarded
$1/3$ cup matzo meal or cracker crumbs
1 egg plus 1 egg white
$1/8$ teaspoon salt
$1/4$ cup vegetable oil

1. In a food processor, shred potato, carrot, and leek.
2. In a large bowl, mix vegetables with matzo meal or cracker crumbs, egg, and salt.
3. Heat 2 tablespoons oil in a large skillet. For each pancake, drop about $1/4$ cup batter into pan and press flat. Brown on both sides, about 5 minutes per side. Drain on paper toweling. Repeat adding more oil to the pan if necessary, until all pancakes are cooked.

Yield: Twelve 3-inch pancakes

· Crispy Potato Fingers ·

Although they take a while to cook, these "fries" are easy to make and nutritionally worth the wait.

2 teaspoons vegetable oil
1 8-ounce baking potato, peeled, cut into strips,
 and placed in a bowl of cold water
Dash of herb seasoning

1. Preheat oven to 450°. Spread oil on baking sheet.
2. Drain and dry potato strips. Place on baking sheet and toss to coat with oil.
3. Sprinkle seasoning on potato strips.
4. Bake for 30 to 45 minutes, taking pan out and loosening and tossing potatoes every 15 minutes.
5. Serve immediately.

Yield: 40 long strips

· Creamed Potatoes ·

Potatoes, milk, and cheese—ingredients comforting and delicious enough to be remembered forever. This dish is nice served with plain meats but can also stand on its own. You might want to improvise by adding a green vegetable in between the layers. Turnips can be substituted for the potatoes, but blanch the turnip slices before composing the gratin.

2 teaspoons margarine
⅓ cup evaporated milk
1 10-to-12-ounce baking potato, peeled and sliced
    in very thin rounds (or 2 medium turnips,
    peeled, sliced, and blanched)
½ cup shredded Swiss cheese (preferably Gruyère)
Dash of pepper and/or ground nutmeg

1. Preheat oven to 375°. Spread 1 teaspoon margarine in bottom of one 6-inch ovenproof dish.
2. Add 1 tablespoon milk to the greased dish.
3. Place half the potatoes in prepared dish, cover with ¼ cup cheese. Repeat the layers.
4. Sprinkle with a dash of pepper and/or nutmeg.
5. Dot with remaining 1 teaspoon margarine.
6. Bake for 30 minutes.
7. Remove from oven. Add remaining milk. Return to oven for an additional 15 minutes.
8. Allow to cool slightly before serving.

Yield: 1 cup

· Sweet Potatoes ·

What can be more appealing than these bright orange, naturally sweet, sweet potatoes? There's no need for additional sweetener and they couldn't be easier to make.

1 large sweet potato, scrubbed (preferably the
    dark-orange variety)
4 tablespoons plain low-fat yogurt
1/4 teaspoon dried tarragon, or 1 teaspoon chopped
    fresh tarragon

1. Preheat oven to 400°.
2. Place potato on a baking sheet and prick with fork. Bake for 45 minutes or until tender.
3. Meanwhile, in a small bowl, combine yogurt and tarragon. Set aside.
4. Remove potato from oven, cut into 4 pieces, remove skin, and dice; or cut potato into 2 pieces and scoop pulp onto 4 plates.
5. Place 1 tablespoon yogurt-tarragon sauce on top of each serving.

Yield: 1 cup

· Sweet Potato Circles ·

Serve Sweet Potato Circles as the starch with dinner or with applesauce for a snack.

4 teaspoons vegetable oil
2 medium sweet potatoes
Salt to taste

1. Heat oven to 450°. Grease a baking sheet with ½ teaspoon oil (or vegetable spray).
2. Peel sweet potatoes. Cut into very thin slices (⅛ to ¼ inch). Place on baking sheet in one layer.
3. Drizzle remaining 3½ teaspoons oil over. Bake for 10 to 15 minutes, until lightly browned (watch carefully). Remove from pan with a spatula. Season and serve.

Yield: 4 servings (about 40 pieces)

·PASTA AND RICE·

·Pasta and Rice Recipes·

"Creamy" Pasta
Fusilli with Creamy Mushroom-Zucchini Sauce
Spaghetti with Cottage Cheese and Strawberries
Quick Fettucini Primavera
Spaghetti with Tomatoes and Peas
Green Fettucini with Tomato–Chick-Pea Sauce
Angel Hair Pasta with Shrimp, Peas, and Cheese
Lola's Roman Pasta
Macaroni and Cottage Cheese Casserole
King Salmon Noodle Pudding
Risotto with Cheese and Vegetables
Quick Fried Rice
Rice and Cheese Balls
Polenta

W hat's low in fat and high in vitamins, minerals, and complex carbohydrate? Pasta, noodles, and rice! There are many shapes and sizes, even colors, to choose from at the grocery store. Most children love spaghetti and macaroni, and it's easy to prepare and inexpensive.

Unlike many recipes for pasta and rice, the recipes in this book do not have excessive amounts of butter or cream. And, unlike packaged rice and pasta mixes, they are low in salt and have no MSG.

In the following recipes, you can use either freshly cooked or reheated pasta.

· "Creamy" Pasta ·

David and Michael can eat this every night for dinner—and it's so easy that I'm tempted to let them! Try adding leftovers for a change or as a nutrient booster.

1 cup cooked pasta
½ teaspoon margarine
¼ cup milk
3 tablespoons Parmesan or Asiago cheese (or more
    for a thicker sauce)

1. In a small bowl, combine pasta and margarine.
2. In a small saucepan, heat milk and pour over pasta.
3. Add cheese and toss. The sauce will be thick and creamy, like Pasta Alfredo.

Yield: 2 servings

· Fusilli with Creamy ·
Mushroom-Zucchini Sauce

This recipe has a texture similar to traditional creamed pasta dishes without all the fat and cholesterol. It is very quick and easy to make.

1 teaspoon olive oil
1/2 cup thin zucchini strips, 1 inch long
1/2 cup finely sliced mushrooms
1/4 cup evaporated milk
2/3 cup cooked fusilli, penne, bows, wheels (red
   pasta is very pretty with this dish)
3 tablespoons grated Parmesan cheese

1. In a small skillet, heat oil. Add zucchini and mushrooms. Stir-fry over medium-high heat for 2 minutes.
2. Reduce heat to low. Stir-fry another minute, until vegetables begin to brown.
3. Add milk. Cook for 30 seconds.
4. Add pasta. Stir to mix and heat through.
5. Sprinkle cheese on top before serving.

Yield: 1 cup

· Spaghetti with Cottage Cheese · and Strawberries

~~~~~~

The colors make this dish visually appealing. You can also prepare bowls the night before and serve cold for breakfast with a glass of milk.

1/2 cup cooked spaghetti, green or white (about 1
    ounce uncooked)
1 teaspoon olive oil
1/4 cup creamed cottage cheese
4 strawberries, diced

1. In a medium-size bowl, mix spaghetti with olive oil.
2. Stir cottage cheese into spaghetti.
3. Stir strawberries into spaghetti mixture and serve, or refrigerate and serve cold.

Yield: 1 serving

· Quick Fettucini Primavera ·

This dish is made almost entirely with leftovers, so it can be thrown together in about five minutes. For very young diners, substitute small pasta (such as pastina, orzo, or alphabets).

2 tablespoons chicken broth
1 small clove garlic, peeled and minced
2 tablespoons olive oil
1/2 cup diced, cooked vegetables (steamed leftover carrots, green beans, broccoli, mushrooms, asparagus)
1 tablespoon chopped fresh basil, or 1/2 teaspoon dried basil
2/3 cup cooked fettucini, cut into 3-inch lengths
3 tablespoons grated Parmesan cheese

1. In a small sauté pan, bring broth to a simmer.
2. Add garlic and cook until broth is evaporated, 1 to 2 minutes, stirring constantly.
3. Add oil, vegetables, basil, and fettucini. Mix together and cook over low heat for 1 to 2 minutes.
4. Sprinkle with Parmesan cheese before serving.

Yield: 1 cup

· Spaghetti with Tomatoes ·
and Peas

A quick, light version of a classic Italian dish.

1 teaspoon margarine
1 cup chopped, drained tomato, fresh or canned
1/2 cup cooked peas
1 tablespoon chopped fresh basil, or 1/2 teaspoon
   dried basil
2/3 cup cooked spaghetti
1/4 cup shredded mozzarella cheese

1. In a small saucepan, melt margarine.
2. Add tomato, peas, and basil, and cook over medium-low heat for 2 to 3 minutes, until heated through.
3. Remove pan from heat. Add spaghetti and toss well.
4. Sprinkle with cheese before serving.

Yield: 1 1/2 cups

·Green Fettucini with Tomato–· Chick-Pea Sauce

This combination of pasta, chick-peas, milk, and cheese makes a high-quality protein dish. The sauce in this recipe is also delicious with the addition of cooked ground meat.

½ cup Rich Tomato Sauce (p. 223), or your favorite
    tomato sauce
¼ cup milk
½ cup canned, drained chick-peas
1 cup cooked green fettucini, cut into 3- to 4-inch
    lengths
¼ cup grated Parmesan cheese

1. In a medium-size saucepan, heat tomato sauce. Add milk. Stir over low heat for 2 to 3 minutes, until warm.
2. Stir in chick-peas.
3. Add fettucini and 2 tablespoons cheese. Toss to coat pasta and heat through.
4. Serve in bowls. Sprinkle some of remaining cheese on each portion.

Yield: 1²/₃ cups

·Angel Hair Pasta with Shrimp,·
Peas, and Cheese

This is a light, colorful, one-dish meal. The sweet peas contrast nicely with the tangy cheese and garlicky shrimp.

1 tablespoon olive oil
1 small clove garlic, peeled and sliced in half
  lengthwise
1 cup small shrimp, shelled and deveined, fresh or
  frozen
1/2 cup defrosted or cooked peas
1 cup cooked angel hair pasta
2 tablespoons mild goat cheese (Montrachet) or
  ricotta cheese
2 teaspoons chopped fresh parsley

1. In a small skillet, heat 1 teaspoon oil over low heat. Add garlic and cook until just beginning to brown, about 2 minutes.
2. Remove garlic. Add shrimp and peas. Increase heat to high and stir-fry for 2 to 3 minutes, until shrimp turn pink.
3. Add pasta and remaining 2 teaspoons oil. Toss well.
4. Top each portion with cheese and parsley.

Yield: 2 cups

· Lola's Roman Pasta ·

The original version uses ground beef, but we also like this dish with leaner ground turkey. Try it either way. Serve with cantaloupe, a glass of milk, and crusty bread. It freezes well.

1/4 cup olive oil
1 medium onion, finely chopped
2 carrots, peeled and finely chopped
1 pound ground turkey (or very lean ground beef)
1 tablespoon dried oregano
1/4 cup chopped fresh parsley
2 tablespoons margarine
1/2 pound cooked fusilli, rotini, or macaroni
1 cup grated Asiago or Parmesan cheese, plus more
   for the table

1. In a large skillet, heat oil. Add onion and carrots and sauté over medium heat for 5 minutes.
2. Add ground turkey. Sauté and stir, breaking apart, until cooked, about 8 minutes.
3. Stir in oregano and parsley. (Mixture can be made in advance up to this point, refrigerated and reheated later in the day.)
4. In a large serving bowl, place margarine.
5. Stir pasta into heated turkey mixture.
6. Pour turkey-pasta mixture into serving bowl. Add cheese. Stir until margarine melts. Serve immediately with extra cheese.

Yield: About 6 cups

· Macaroni and Cottage Cheese ·
Casserole

This easy casserole, adapted from More Recipes from the Wooden Door *by Healthmere Press (1985), can be prepared ahead and then baked. Try serving it with crunchy carrot sticks or sweet honeydew slices.*

2 1/2 teaspoons vegetable oil
1/4 cup chopped green pepper
1/4 cup chopped onion
1/4 cup chopped celery
1 clove garlic, peeled and minced
1 3/4 cups water
1/3 cup tomato paste
1 cup uncooked elbow macaroni
1/2 teaspoon dried oregano
1/4 teaspoon salt, if desired
2 tablespoons chopped fresh parsley
1 1/2 cups cottage cheese, drained
3 tablespoons shredded cheddar cheese

1. Preheat oven to 350°. Grease a medium-size baking dish with 1/2 teaspoon oil (or vegetable spray).
2. In a small saucepan, heat remaining 2 teaspoons oil. Add green pepper, onion, celery, and garlic. Sauté over medium heat until tender, about 2 minutes.
3. Stir in water, tomato paste, macaroni, and oregano, and salt, if desired.
4. Bring to boil. Reduce to a simmer. Cover and cook, stirring occasionally, until macaroni is tender, about 10 minutes.
5. Add parsley.
6. Spoon half the macaroni mixture into the prepared baking dish. Top with half the cottage cheese. Sprinkle on half the cheddar

cheese. Repeat with remaining macaroni mixture, cottage cheese, and cheddar.

7. Bake until bubbly and golden, about 15 minutes.

Yield: 3 cups

·King Salmon Noodle Pudding·

♈♈

Here is another casserole dish that uses leftovers. If you use canned salmon, be sure to mash in the soft, edible bones, which are a terrific source of calcium.

1 teaspoon margarine
¹/₂ cup cooked elbow macaroni (¹/₄ cup uncooked)
¹/₄ cup cooked or canned salmon, flaked
1 tablespoon plain, low-fat yogurt
1 tablespoon cottage cheese
2 tablespoons cooked vegetables (broccoli, peas, carrots)
1 egg
2 tablespoons grated mozzarella cheese
2 teaspoons unsweetened corn or bran flakes

1. Preheat oven to 375°. Lightly grease two 3-inch soufflé dishes with ¹/₂ teaspoon margarine (or vegetable spray).
2. In a medium-size bowl, mix macaroni, salmon, yogurt, cottage cheese, vegetables, and egg.
3. Divide mixture into the prepared dishes.
4. Sprinkle cheese on top. Crumble cereal over cheese. Dot with remaining ¹/₂ teaspoon margarine.
5. Bake for 20 minutes, until golden and bubbling.

Yield: 1 cup

· Risotto with Cheese and · Vegetables

The bright-yellow color of saffron in this Northern Italian specialty appeals to many children. The sticky consistency makes the rice easy to eat. To increase the nutritional value of this recipe, you may substitute brown rice, which has more fiber, vitamins, and minerals than white rice.

1 tablespoon olive oil
1 tablespoon finely chopped onion
$^1/_3$ cup raw arborio rice
2 cups chicken broth (preferably unsalted)
$^1/_4$ teaspoon saffron, if desired
$^1/_2$ cup grated Parmesan cheese or shredded
  mozzarella cheese
$^1/_2$ cup chopped, cooked vegetables (use leftovers)
Parmesan cheese for topping

1. In a medium-size saucepan, heat oil.
2. Add onion and cook over medium heat until tender but not browned, about 2 minutes.
3. Add rice and cook until opaque, about 1 minute.
4. Add $^1/_2$ cup broth and cook over medium-low heat, stirring occasionally, until liquid has almost evaporated. Continue adding broth, $^1/_2$ cup at a time, stirring occasionally, until rice is cooked. Add saffron, if desired, in the last $^1/_2$ cup broth.
5. Stir in cheese and vegetables.
6. Serve sprinkled with Parmesan cheese.

Yield: 1 cup

· Quick Fried Rice ·

‿‿‿‿‿‿‿‿‿‿‿‿‿‿‿‿‿‿‿‿‿‿‿‿‿‿‿‿‿‿‿‿‿‿‿‿

An Oriental rice dish perfect with drained and sautéed or broiled tofu or with Speared Poultry (see page 189). You can also add bits of meat, chicken, fish, poultry, or egg to the rice for a complete dinner.

1½ tablespoons peanut oil
½ cup chopped, cooked vegetables (carrots,
    Brussels sprouts, peas)
¼ cup finely chopped green onion
1 cup cooked rice
2 teaspoons reduced-sodium soy sauce (or 1
    teaspoon soy sauce mixed with 1 teaspoon water)

1. In a small skillet, heat oil.
2. Add vegetables and onion and stir to coat. Cook over medium heat for about 1 minute.
3. Add rice and soy sauce. Stir and serve.

Yield: 1½ cups

·Rice and Cheese Balls·

These crispy finger treats are an adaptation of an Italian recipe for suppli. The originals are deep-fried. Ours are baked. They will be crispy on the outside with melted cheese on the inside. Serve alone or with your favorite tomato sauce and garnish with chopped parsley. They can be frozen and reheated. This is a great way to use leftover rice from Chinese carry-out.

2 tablespoons olive oil
1 cup cooked arborio or Chinese rice (both are very
  sticky when cooked)
1 egg, lightly beaten
$1/2$ cup dry, fine plain bread crumbs
Twelve $1/2$-inch cubes mozzarella or Swiss cheese
1 tablespoon chopped fresh parsley

Optional: $1/4$ cup tomato sauce

1. Preheat oven to 400°. Grease a baking sheet with $1/2$ teaspoon olive oil (or vegetable spray).
2. In a medium-size bowl, combine rice and egg.
3. Spread bread crumbs in a shallow dish.
4. Using a teaspoon, scoop up some rice mixture (it will be very sticky). Place a cube of cheese on top. Using a second teaspoon, scoop up some more rice and press on top of rice and cheese. Form into a ball with wet hands.
5. Roll the ball in bread crumbs and place on baking sheet.
6. Continue to shape into 12 balls. Rice balls can be refrigerated at this point.
7. Drizzle remaining $5 1/2$ teaspoons oil over the balls and bake for 40 minutes. Turn the balls over and bake an additional 20 minutes, or until golden brown and crunchy.
8. Serve warm with chopped parsley, and tomato sauce, if desired.

Yield: 12 balls, each about 2 inches in diameter

· Polenta ·

ᴝᴝᴝᴝᴝᴝᴝᴝᴝᴝᴝᴝᴝ

*The best polenta I've eaten was served with cuttlefish stew at La Ma-
donna in Venice. This version is cooked with milk (although you can use water
or broth). Be sure to buy enriched cornmeal. It adds iron and B vitamins to
your family's diet.*

2 cups milk, water, or broth
¾ cup yellow cornmeal
⅓ cup grated Parmesan cheese
⅓ cup shredded mozzarella cheese

Optional: 2 tablespoons olive oil

1. In a medium-size, heavy saucepan, bring milk to a boil over
   moderate heat.
2. Very gradually add cornmeal, stirring constantly.
3. Reduce heat to very low and cook, stirring constantly, while
   mixture thickens, 10 to 15 minutes.
4. Add cheeses and stir until melted.
5. Lightly sprinkle a 10-by-12-inch piece of aluminum foil with cold
   water. Spread or pat the cornmeal mixture into a rectangle on the
   foil. Refrigerate for at least 1 hour.
6. To serve, cut in squares or triangles. Serve cold, or brush with oil
   and grill or broil until brown, about 5 minutes. Or cover and bake
   in a low oven until warm, about 10 minutes.

Yield: 12 to 16 pieces

·MEAT·

· Meat Recipes ·

Broccoli Burgers
Reina's Grandma's Pretty Neat Sloppy Joes
Herbed Steak Package
Savory Veal Loaves
Braised Veal Shanks
Veal Piccata
Tasty Tender Liver
Lamb Meatballs
Foil-Cooked Lamb
Lamb Choplets
Basil Mustard Pork
Pork and Prunes

Lean red meat is the best source of dietary iron. For reasons not entirely understood, the body absorbs the iron in meat far better than the iron in grains, eggs, vegetables, or even fish. In addition to the iron provided by the meat itself, red meats, poultry, and fish all enhance the absorption of iron from other foods eaten at the same meal.

Today, red meat is sold well trimmed of visible fat. Minimize the amount of edible fat by broiling, grilling, or roasting meat. Use a nonstick pan and add only small amounts of fat to sauté or stir-fry meat.

If your child balks at eating meat because it is hard to chew, cut it into small strips or cubes. And don't overcook it, for it dries out and becomes tough. Ground meat formed into meatballs, patties, or loaves is a favorite of young children.

· Broccoli Burgers ·

Everyone loves hamburgers! These child-sized burgers laced with broccoli are good served on miniature whole-grain rolls, with Crispy Potato Fingers (see page 151) and Creamy Cole Slaw (see page 116).

> ¼ pound ground round steak
> 2 tablespoons finely chopped, cooked broccoli (or other vegetable)
> ¼ teaspoon dried thyme
> 2 thin slices cheese (Swiss, cheddar, or other favorite)

1. Preheat grill or broiler on high heat.
2. In a small bowl, combine beef, broccoli, and thyme.
3. Form beef mixture into 2 small patties.
4. Cook until desired doneness.
5. Place cheese on top of meat patties just before done. Cook for 30 seconds more, or until cheese melts.

Yield: 2 burgers

·Reina's Grandma's·
Pretty Neat Sloppy Joes

Almost all children adore Sloppy Joes. They make an excellent party dish served over Herb Bran Muffins (see page 261) or Polenta (see page 170), or mixed with macaroni. The recipe freezes well for a quick meal.

1 tablespoon vegetable oil
1 large onion or ½ Spanish onion, finely chopped
1 sweet red or green pepper, finely chopped
3 carrots, peeled and chopped
1¼ pounds lean ground beef
1 6-ounce can tomato paste (⅔ cup)
2 tablespoons ketchup
2 tablespoons Dijon mustard
1 tablespoon cider vinegar
1 teaspoon sugar
2 to 3 cups water or tomato juice

1. In a medium saucepan, heat oil.
2. Add onion, pepper, and carrots. Cook over medium heat until softened, about 2 minutes.
3. Add meat and brown over medium-high heat, stirring and breaking meat into fine pieces.
4. Pour off any fat.
5. Add tomato paste, ketchup, mustard, vinegar, and sugar. Stir well. Add 2 cups water or tomato juice.
6. Simmer over very low heat, stirring occasionally, for 45 to 50 minutes. Add more liquid, if necessary. The mixture should be very thick.

NOTE: Freeze in covered plastic containers or in individual portions by placing mixture in small muffin cups or ice cube trays. Freeze, remove from muffin cups or ice cube trays, and refreeze in plastic freezer bags.

Yield: About 3 cups

· Herbed Steak Package ·

Serve this steak alone or with Creamy Tomato Dip (see page 224) or mashed avocado and mild salsa.

1/2 teaspoon vegetable oil
2 ounces lean New York strip or sirloin steak, cut into 1/2-inch cubes
1 shallot or green onion, finely minced
1/8 teaspoon dried oregano or basil
Squeeze of fresh lemon

1. Preheat oven to 450°. Prepare a foil package by cutting a piece of aluminum foil 4 by 12 inches wide. Spread oil on foil.
2. In a small bowl, mix steak, shallot or onion, herb, and lemon. Place mixture on foil. Fold up foil package tightly.
3. Bake for 10 minutes.

Yield: 1 serving

· Savory Veal Loaves ·

These meat loaves have an unusual, slightly sweet, savory taste. They're delicious warm or cold and can be frozen. Serve with Creamed Potatoes (see page 152) or New Potatoes Vinaigrette (see page 118).

1 slice whole-grain bread
1/2 cup milk
1 tablespoon vegetable oil
1/4 cup finely chopped onion
1/3 cup finely chopped mushrooms
3/4 pound lean ground veal
1/4 pound lean ground pork
2 tablespoons chopped fresh parsley
1/2 teaspoon dried thyme
1/4 teaspoon ground nutmeg
1/8 teaspoon salt
Pinch of pepper
1 egg
1/2 cup chopped banana (1 banana)

1. Preheat oven to 375°.
2. In a small bowl, soak bread in milk. Set aside.
3. In a large skillet, heat oil. Add onion and mushrooms and sauté over medium-high heat, stirring constantly, until softened, about 3 minutes.
4. Remove skillet from heat. Add veal, pork, parsley, thyme, nutmeg, salt, and pepper. Stir well.
5. Add egg and bread-milk mixture. Stir well, mashing bread.
6. Add banana. Stir to mix. The mixture will be rather loose.
7. Spoon meat into 5 mini-loaf pans or 12 muffin cups.
8. Place in oven. Bake for 45 minutes for mini-loaves or 30 minutes

for muffin-size loaves, until firm. Cool for 10 minutes before slicing or refrigerate or freeze for later use.

Yield: 5 mini-loaves or 12 muffin-size loaves

· Braised Veal Shanks ·

This is a wonderful family dish for cold days that can be made with veal or lamb shanks. Serve with rice, noodles, or mashed potatoes. It freezes well.

3 tablespoons olive oil
1/2 cup flour
4 veal shanks, 2 to 2 1/2 inches thick
3 tablespoons tomato paste
2 cups chicken or beef broth
4 medium carrots, peeled and diced
2 stalks celery, diced
1 medium onion, diced
4 cloves garlic, peeled and chopped
1 cup chopped fresh parsley
1 teaspoon dried thyme

1. In a large skillet or Dutch oven, warm oil over medium-high heat.
2. In a shallow dish, place flour. Roll each veal shank in flour. Shake off excess. Place veal in skillet and brown on all sides.
3. In a small bowl, stir tomato paste into 1 cup broth. Add to veal shanks.
4. Add carrots, celery, onion, garlic, parsley, and thyme. Cover and simmer for 30 minutes.
5. Remove cover. Turn veal shanks. Add remaining broth. Cover and cook for 30 minutes longer.

Yield: 4 veal shanks (6 to 8 servings)

·Veal Piccata·

A quick way to prepare veal scallopini. Raw, sliced turkey breast may be substituted for the veal.

2 tablespoons flour
1 egg
¼ cup dried bread crumbs
¼ pound veal scallopini, very thinly sliced (2 to 4 pieces)
2 teaspoons olive oil
1 teaspoon margarine
½ teaspoon lemon juice
2 teaspoons chopped fresh parsley

1. In a shallow dish, place flour.
2. In a second shallow dish, beat egg.
3. In a third shallow dish, place crumbs.
4. Dip each piece of veal in flour. Shake off excess, dip in egg, then dip in bread crumbs.
5. In a skillet, heat oil and margarine.
6. Add veal to skillet and cook until browned. Turn and cook until browned on other side, about 5 minutes total.
7. Squeeze lemon juice over veal.
8. Cut into bite-size portions and sprinkle with parsley.

Yield: About ¹/₂ cup

· Tasty Tender Liver ·

Liver is the richest source of iron and vitamin A that you or your child can eat. This preparation ensures a juicy and tender piece of liver. The packages can be made ahead and refrigerated until cooking time.

$1/4$ pound baby beef or calves' liver (1 average
  slice—$7^1/_2$ inches by $2^1/_2$ inches by $1/4$ inch)
1 teaspoon finely chopped onion
1 teaspoon fresh chopped parsley
1 tablespoon chopped carrot
$1/8$ teaspoon dried thyme
$1/4$ bay leaf
1 teaspoon olive oil
$1/4$ teaspoon vinegar

1. Preheat oven to 450°.
2. Cut a piece of aluminum foil large enough to enclose liver.
3. Place liver on foil. Top with remaining ingredients.
4. Fold up package.
5. Place in oven for 10 minutes.
6. To serve, remove bay leaf and cut liver into bite-size pieces. Arrange on plate with some vegetables and juice on top.

Yield: About 1 cup

· Lamb Meatballs ·

Lamb Meatballs have an unusual, appealing flavor. They go well with rice or pasta, and can be served warm with tomato sauce or cold in a pita, accompanied by carrot sticks or Dilled Carrot Salad (see page 113). Baked meatballs freeze well and can be reheated quickly in the oven or a microwave.

1/2 pound ground lamb
1/2 cup shredded zucchini (half a medium zucchini)
1 tablespoon chopped fresh mint, or 1/2 teaspoon
  dried mint
1 clove garlic, peeled and minced
2 teaspoons chopped fresh parsley
2 tablespoons tomato paste
1/2 teaspoon dried oregano
1 egg
Dash of salt and pepper
1/2 cup dried bread crumbs

1. Preheat oven to 450°.
2. In a large bowl, mix all ingredients except 1/4 cup bread crumbs.
3. Spread remaining 1/4 cup bread crumbs in a shallow dish.
4. Form meat mixture into 1-inch balls.
5. Roll each ball in bread crumbs and place on baking sheet.
6. Bake for 10 minutes. Turn and bake for 3 to 5 minutes longer.

Yield: Fifteen 1-inch balls

· Foil-Cooked Lamb ·

We have an annual summer barbecue when we roast a whole leg of lamb over an outdoor fire. I slice small pieces of meat off the leg and prepare this quick recipe for the boys in advance. That way they can eat, even if we're not quite ready. Cooking in foil results in a very tender and juicy piece of meat. Good accompaniments are Dilled Carrot Salad (see page 113), Brown Rice Salad with Peas (see page 122), or Lentil Salad (see page 119), greens, and crisp bread. Try serving with Creamy Tomato Dip (see page 224) or Aioli Sauce (see page 226).

$1/2$ teaspoon olive oil
2 ounces leg, loin, or saddle of lamb, or meat from
   1 lamb chop, cut into bite-size pieces (about $1/2$
   cup)
$1/2$ clove garlic, peeled and thinly sliced
$1/2$ teaspoon dried rosemary
$1/4$ teaspoon lemon juice

1. Prepare a foil package by cutting a piece of aluminum foil about 4 inches by 12 inches. Spread oil on foil.
2. In a small bowl, combine remaining ingredients.
3. Place lamb mixture on foil package. Fold tightly and marinate in the refrigerator for several hours.
4. Roast in preheated 450° oven or on barbecue grill for 10 minutes.

Yield: 1 serving (about $1/2$ cup)

· Lamb Choplets ·

Children over three can pick up a chop and chew the meat right off the bone. Serve with a small bowl of Creamy Tomato Dip (see page 224) or mint jelly.

> 2 very thin rib lamb chops with rib bone (¼ to ½
>   inch thick)
> 1 sprig fresh rosemary, or ½ teaspoon dried
>   rosemary
> 1 clove garlic, peeled and sliced
> ½ teaspoon olive oil
> Salt and pepper to taste

1. Trim all fat off lamb chops.
2. If using fresh rosemary, cut rosemary into 4 pieces.
3. On a plate, sprinkle half the rosemary, half the garlic, and half the oil. Place lamb chops on top. Sprinkle remaining rosemary, garlic, and oil over chops. Salt and pepper to taste. Cover with plastic wrap and let stand at room temperature for 1 hour or refrigerate for up to 24 hours. Bring to room temperature before cooking.
4. Preheat broiler. Broil lamb chops for 5 minutes. Turn, then broil for 3 to 5 minutes longer. Remove from broiler and cool slightly. (Cut meat into bite-size pieces for younger children.)

Yield: 2 chops (1 serving)

·Basil Mustard Pork·

This is reminiscent of Mediterranean barbecues. Serve with fresh, sliced tomatoes and Creamed Potatoes (see page 152). Leftovers make delicious sandwiches.

3/4 pound pork tenderloin
3 teaspoons Dijon mustard
3 teaspoons olive oil
1 clove garlic, peeled and minced
3 tablespoons chopped fresh basil, or 1 1/2 teaspoons
dried basil

1. Preheat broiler or grill.
2. Slice pork crosswise into 1/2-inch slices.
3. Mix mustard, oil, garlic, and basil.
4. Using half the mustard mixture, spread a little on top of each pork slice. Place under broiler or on grill. Cook for 10 minutes, until browned. Turn. Spread remaining mustard mixture on pork slices. Cook for another 5 minutes, until browned.

Yield: 12 to 14 slices

· Pork and Prunes ·

Lean pork is an excellent source of the B vitamin thiamin. The prunes add sweetness and many additional vitamins and minerals to this tender dish. Serve with plain noodles or Pureed Parsnips and Cauliflower (see page 147).

3/4 pound pork tenderloin, butterflied
12 pitted prunes
1/8 teaspoon ground cinnamon
1 1/2 teaspoons vegetable oil
3/4 cup pear or prune juice
3/4 cup broth (any kind) or water

Optional: 1/3 cup evaporated milk

1. Preheat oven to 350°.
2. Place pork, cut side up, on a plate. Arrange prunes in center, sprinkle with cinnamon, and roll up pork, jelly-roll fashion. Secure with toothpicks or with 1-inch pieces of spaghetti. (Carefully push the spaghetti into meat. It will work like a toothpick, holding the roll together, and does not need to be removed before serving.)
3. In a medium-size skillet or flameproof baking pan, heat oil over medium-high heat.
4. Brown pork on all sides.
5. Add juice and broth or water. Cover and place in oven.
6. Cook for 20 minutes.
7. Remove pork to a plate. Slice.
8. Boil juice over high heat, stirring constantly, until thickened. If desired, add evaporated milk.
9. Pour sauce over pork and serve, making sure each piece of meat has some prune with it. Remove toothpicks before serving.

Yield: 6 to 8 slices

·POULTRY·

· Poultry Recipes ·

Golden Chicken Nuggets
Crunchy Chicken Drumsticks
Speared Poultry
Foil-Cooked Chicken
Grandma Nettie's Chicken
White Chicken or Veal Stew
Undercover Poultry
Chicken or Fish with Artichoke Hearts
Cold Poultry with Creamy Tomato Dip
Sweet Chicken Salad
Sautéed Chicken Livers
Orange Chicken Livers
Rolled Turkey Breast
Steamed Turkey Rolls
Turkey-Grape Salad

P oultry is quick, easy, and economical to prepare. It is also an excellent low-fat source of protein, B vitamins, and minerals. Best of all, most children love it!

To avoid salmonella food poisoning, wash with hot, soapy water the cutting board, all utensils, sink, and countertops that come into contact with raw chicken, then rinse and dry. If you cut chicken on a board and do not wash the board before using it to cut salad ingredients that will not be cooked, the salad may become contaminated.

Also, be sure to cook poultry thoroughly. If you stuff chicken or turkey with dressing, allow extra cooking time. If there are leftovers, remove the dressing before refrigerating the bird.

Many grocery stores sell cooked chicken prepared on a rotisserie. These spit-roasted chickens can be real time-savers when you need cooked chicken for a recipe or for plain roasted chicken for a snack or sandwich.

· Golden Chicken Nuggets ·

Here is a nutritious and easy version of a fast-food favorite. Because it is very soft (rather than crispy), it is especially good for young children.

2 teaspoons vegetable oil
1/4 cup plain low-fat yogurt
1/2 cup dry baby oatmeal with bananas
1/2 teaspoon herb seasoning
1 whole chicken breast, skinned, boned, and cut
 into bite-size pieces

1. Preheat oven to 400°. Use 1/2 teaspoon oil to grease a baking sheet.
2. Place yogurt in a shallow dish. In another shallow dish, mix dry baby oatmeal and herb seasoning.
3. Coat chicken with yogurt, then roll in seasoned oatmeal.

4. Place chicken on prepared pan. Sprinkle with remaining oil.
5. Bake for 10 minutes, until cooked through.

Yield: 1 cup

·Crunchy Chicken Drumsticks·

ᱹᱹᱹ

David, Michael, and their father all devoured these drumsticks. You can easily increase the amounts for a large crowd, making this excellent party fare.

2½ tablespoons peanut oil
6 chicken legs or 8 chicken wings (meaty part only)
¼ cup ground, roasted, unsalted nuts
¼ cup seasoned bread crumbs

1. Preheat oven to 350°. Grease a baking sheet with ½ tablespoon oil (or vegetable spray).
2. Remove skin from chicken.
3. In a shallow dish, mix nuts and crumbs.
4. In a second shallow dish, place remaining 2 tablespoons oil.
5. Roll chicken in oil, then in nut-crumb mixture. Place pieces on cookie sheet.
6. Bake 1 hour for legs, 50 minutes for wings.

Yield: 6 legs or 8 wings

· Speared Poultry ·

We guarantee that this will become a favorite. This dish is good with Quick Fried Rice (see page 168) and crispy red and green pepper strips.

1 tablespoon lemon juice
1 teaspoon vegetable oil
1/2 teaspoon honey or brown sugar
1/8 teaspoon garlic powder
1/2 teaspoon soy sauce or teriyaki sauce (preferably reduced sodium)
1 chicken breast, boned, skinned, and cut in cubes, or 1 cup diced turkey breast
8 pineapple chunks

1. In a nonmetallic bowl, whisk together all ingredients except chicken and pineapple.
2. Stir in chicken cubes, cover, and marinate for 2 hours or overnight in the refrigerator.
3. Alternate chicken and pineapple on each of 2 skewers.
4. Grill or broil until done, 3 to 5 minutes, turning and checking often. Remove from skewers before serving.

Yield: 2 skewers

· Foil-Cooked Chicken ·

Basil gives a unique flavor to a very easy chicken dish.

1 teaspoon olive oil
½ chicken breast, skinned and boned, or 1
   drumstick
¼ teaspoon dried basil, or 2 teaspoons chopped
   fresh basil
1 tablespoon chopped fresh spinach leaves
2 mushrooms, chopped
½ carrot, peeled and chopped

1. Preheat oven to 450°. Cut a strip of aluminum foil, about 4 by 12 inches. Spread ½ teaspoon oil on the center third of foil.
2. Cut chicken into bite-size pieces or use whole drumstick. Place on oiled section of foil.
3. Sprinkle basil, spinach, mushrooms, and carrot over chicken.
4. Drizzle with remaining oil.
5. Fold foil into a package. Place in oven. Bake chicken breast for 15 minutes, drumstick for 20 minutes.

Yield: 1 serving (about ⅔ cup)

· Grandma Nettie's Chicken ·

This is adapted from a family recipe of our friend Alex, whose great-grandmother was from Italy.

1 teaspoon olive or vegetable oil
1 whole chicken breast, skinned, boned, and diced
  (about 1 cup)
2 small new potatoes, peeled and diced
½ carrot, peeled and sliced
1 clove garlic, peeled and minced
½ teaspoon dried basil, or 1 tablespoon chopped
  fresh basil
½ teaspoon dried oregano
1 can (14 ounces) Italian tomatoes, crushed and
  drained, or 3 fresh, ripe tomatoes, chopped
3 tablespoons grated Parmesan cheese

1. Preheat oven to 375°.
2. Heat oil in a medium-size ovenproof skillet.
3. Add chicken, potatoes, and carrots and cook, stirring constantly, over medium-high heat until chicken is lightly browned, 3 to 5 minutes.
4. Remove skillet from heat. Stir in garlic.
5. Cover skillet. Place in oven. Bake for 15 minutes.
6. Remove from oven. Stir in basil and oregano.
7. Spoon crushed or chopped tomatoes over chicken mixture.
8. Sprinkle cheese on top.
9. Return to oven. Bake uncovered for 10 minutes, or until cheese is melted.

Yield: 2 cups

· White Chicken or Veal Stew ·

In Nurieux, France, there is a roadside "diner" serving delicious, hearty, home-style meals. The following recipe is reminiscent of its creamy stew. Serve over wide egg noodles or cut-up fettucini.

1 tablespoon vegetable oil
1 tablespoon finely chopped sweet red pepper
1 tablespoon finely chopped sweet green pepper
1 small green onion, finely chopped
1 cup cubed chicken breast or veal loin
6 small green beans, ends trimmed
1 small carrot, peeled and sliced into $\frac{1}{8}$-inch rounds
$\frac{1}{2}$ cup chicken broth (plus $\frac{1}{4}$ cup, if necessary)
$\frac{1}{4}$ cup evaporated milk
$\frac{1}{2}$ teaspoon snipped chives or chopped fresh parsley

1. In a small saucepan, heat oil.
2. Add peppers and onion and sauté over medium heat for 2 minutes.
3. Add chicken or veal and cook for about 1 minute, until white on all sides.
4. Add green beans, carrot, and $\frac{1}{2}$ cup broth. Bring to a boil. Reduce to a simmer; cover, and cook over low heat for 8 to 10 minutes until meat is cooked thoroughly.
5. Remove chicken or veal and vegetables to a plate.
6. If necessary, add more broth to sauce.
7. Bring to a boil. Reduce to a simmer.
8. Add milk and chicken or veal and vegetables to pan. Stir to coat with sauce and heat through.

Yield: 2 cups

· Undercover Poultry ·

The following can be prepared in one large pan or in individual 3-inch baking dishes. Serve with something colorful and crunchy—carrot salad, fresh grapes, or apple slices.

1 tablespoon vegetable oil
1 recipe Quick Cream Sauce (p. 230)
Pinch of each: cayenne, nutmeg, herb seasoning
1 tablespoon chopped green onion
1/2 cup chopped spinach
1/2 cup chopped mushrooms
1/4 cup cooked rice
1/2 cup diced, cooked poultry
2 tablespoons shredded mozzarella cheese

1. Preheat oven to 400°. Lightly grease 2 small soufflé cups with 1 teaspoon oil (or vegetable spray).
2. Heat the cream sauce. Remove from heat, add spices, and set aside.
3. In a small skillet, heat remaining 2 teaspoons oil. Add onion, spinach, and mushrooms. Sauté over medium heat until softened, about 3 minutes.
4. In a medium-size bowl, mix vegetables, rice, and poultry. Pour into prepared dishes.
5. Spoon cream sauce over vegetable-poultry mixture and top with shredded cheese.
6. Bake for 10 minutes, until bubbly and golden.

Yield: 1 cup

· Chicken or Fish with ·
Artichoke Hearts

The combination of garlic, olive oil, and artichoke hearts reminds me of northern Italy in the spring. Round out the meal with Risotto with Cheese and Vegetables (see page 167) or Spaghetti with Tomatoes and Peas (see page 161).

1 tablespoon lemon juice
1 tablespoon olive oil
1 large clove garlic, peeled and minced
¼ cup chopped fresh parsley
1 whole chicken breast, halved, skinned, and
  boned, or ½ pound white fish fillet, well boned
4 artichoke hearts, fresh, frozen, or canned
  (rinsed), thinly sliced

1. In a medium-size bowl, mix lemon juice, oil, garlic, and parsley.
2. Add chicken or fish and artichokes.
3. If using chicken, marinate several hours or overnight in the refrigerator. If using fish, marinate half an hour in the refrigerator.
4. Preheat oven to 375°.
5. In a medium-size baking dish, place chicken or fish and artichokes. Cover with remaining marinade.
6. Cover dish. Bake for 30 minutes for chicken or 10 minutes for fish.

Yield: 1½ cups

· Cold Poultry with Creamy ·
Tomato Dip

Here is a refreshing way to use leftover poultry. The sauce adds color as well as flavor to the plate. Your child will have three different textures to explore. Serve with toast or Cheese Crouton Strips (see page 101).

1/4 cup cold cooked chicken or turkey
2 tablespoons peeled, seeded, and thinly sliced cucumber
1 recipe Creamy Tomato Dip (p. 224) made with mint
2 mint leaves, or 2 sprigs fresh parsley

1. Cut poultry into bite-size pieces.
2. On one side of a plate, arrange the poultry.
3. Arrange cucumber on other side.
4. Spoon sauce attractively down the center.
5. Garnish with mint leaves or parsley.

Yield: About 1/2 cup

· Sweet Chicken Salad ·

Try this salad as a nice summer dinner served with crunchy lettuce, cheese, Italian bread or whole-wheat pita, and seasonal fruit. Remember our advice about choking, and do not serve this to children under three.

1 tablespoon olive oil
$^{1}/_{2}$ teaspoon vinegar
$^{1}/_{2}$ teaspoon lemon juice
$^{1}/_{2}$ teaspoon sugar
$^{1}/_{4}$ teaspoon ground ginger or cinnamon
Dash of freshly ground pepper
1 cup cooked diced chicken
$^{1}/_{2}$ tablespoon pine nuts
1 tablespoon golden raisins

1. In a medium-size bowl, mix oil, vinegar, lemon juice, sugar, and spices.
2. Add chicken, pine nuts, and raisins.
3. Toss mixture lightly, and refrigerate overnight.

Yield: About 1 cup

· Sautéed Chicken Livers ·

Chicken livers, carrots, green pepper, and parsley are all rich sources of vitamin A, which keeps membranes strong, protects against infections, and encourages bone growth. Chicken livers are also a rich source of iron. Puree leftovers and use as a spread with crackers or apple wedges.

1/2 pound chicken livers
2 teaspoons margarine
2 teaspoons vegetable oil
1 cup chopped onion
1 cup chopped carrot
1 cup chopped sweet green pepper
1 cup chopped mushrooms
2 tablespoons chopped fresh parsley
1 cup chicken broth

1. Wash, dry, and dice chicken livers.
2. In a medium-size skillet, heat margarine and oil. Add onion, carrot, green pepper, and mushrooms and cook over medium-high heat until softened, about 3 minutes.
3. Add livers and cook for 2 minutes.
4. Add parsley and broth and cook until liquid thickens, about 5 minutes.

Yield: 1 1/2 to 2 cups

·Orange Chicken Livers·

Sweet tastes appeal to children. This almost caramelized dish is a new way to offer a nutrient-rich meal.

1 tablespoon sugar
2 teaspoons white vinegar
¹/₂ cup orange juice
¹/₂ pound chicken livers, cleaned, dried, and diced
¹/₃ cup finely julienned carrots
1 orange, seeded, halved, and cut into thin
    "smiles" or peeled and segmented, or ¹/₂ cup
    drained mandarin oranges

1. In a medium-size heavy saucepan, combine sugar and vinegar. Cook over moderate heat, stirring constantly, until mixture becomes a deep golden caramel color.
2. Remove from heat. Stir in orange juice, chicken livers, and carrots.
3. Return to heat and bring to a boil. Reduce to a simmer. Cover and cook for about 5 minutes, until livers are cooked through.
4. To serve, spoon some livers on a plate, and garnish with oranges.

Yield: 1¹/₂ cups

·Rolled Turkey Breast·

You can cook the turkey the day before and serve it again, cold, with Golden Dippy Sauce (see page 225) or in sandwiches. Leftovers freeze well.

2 cups (¼ pound) fresh spinach, well washed
2 to 3 cloves garlic, peeled
1 2¼- to 2½-pound turkey breast, boned and
   butterflied
Salt and pepper to taste
4 sprigs fresh rosemary, or 1 tablespoon dried
   rosemary
1 tablespoon olive oil

1. Preheat oven to 325°.
2. In a food processor, coarsely chop spinach and garlic.
3. On a board, place turkey, skin side down. Season lightly with salt and pepper. Spread spinach-garlic mixture along one of the long ends. Roll up turkey, jelly-roll fashion. Secure with short skewers or toothpicks; then tie with string.
4. Place 2 sprigs fresh or ½ tablespoon dried rosemary on the bottom of a baking pan. Place turkey on top. Drizzle oil over. Place remaining rosemary on top.
5. Bake for 1¾ to 2 hours, until golden brown.
6. Serve warm, or chill and slice. Remove skewers or toothpicks before serving.

Yield: 10 to 12 slices (¼ inch thick)

· Steamed Turkey Rolls ·

This dish was inspired by a dinner we ate at Le Priore in Avignon several years ago.

1 medium carrot, peeled and julienned
½ cup chopped spinach leaves, well washed
2-inch piece green onion, julienned
2 mushrooms, thinly sliced
½ teaspoon dried thyme
Pinch of herb seasoning
2 thin slices raw turkey breast (about 4 ounces)
2 pieces spaghetti (uncooked)

1. In a small bowl, mix carrot, spinach, onion, mushrooms, thyme, and herb seasoning.
2. Spoon vegetable mixture onto turkey and roll up, jelly-roll fashion, as tightly as possible. Secure with 1-inch pieces of spaghetti. (Carefully push spaghetti into turkey. It will work like a toothpick, holding the roll together.)
3. Place turkey rolls in a steamer (a simple steamer basket in a pot works well) and place over boiling water. Cover and steam for 20 minutes.
4. Remove from steamer and slice in half or quarters.

Yield: 2 servings

· Turkey-Grape Salad ·

When you prepare a whole turkey, there are often leftovers. Turn them into this delightful salad.

1 tablespoon plain low-fat yogurt
2 teaspoons mayonnaise
1/2 teaspoon Dijon mustard
1/2 teaspoon peach or apricot jam
2/3 cup diced, cooked turkey breast (or chicken)
1/3 cup seedless grapes, halved or quartered
2 tablespoons diced celery

Optional: 1 tablespoon ground toasted hazelnuts or
            almonds
            Crunchy Chinese noodles

1. In a medium-size bowl, combine yogurt, mayonnaise, mustard, and jam.
2. Add turkey, grapes, and celery. Toss well to combine.
3. Sprinkle with nuts, if desired. Chill.
4. Serve with crunchy Chinese noodles, if desired, or in a sandwich.

Yield: 1 cup

·SEAFOOD·

· Seafood Recipes ·

Swordfish and Nectarine Brochette
Fancy Sole
Stuffed Fish Fillets
Poached Salmon with Peas and Cucumbers
Salmon Bits
Sea Squares
Fish Balls
Tuna and Bean Smash
Tuna Provençal
Mediterranean Monkfish
Fish Hash
Breaded Bay Scallops
Sautéed Rock Shrimp
Shrimp Salad
Sardine Spread

W hen purchasing fresh fish, ask the fishmonger to be especially careful about removing bones because you are cooking it for your youngster. Some varieties of fish used in these recipes have large bones that are easy to remove. Shellfish, such as scallops and shrimp, are popular, though expensive, for young diners. Their shape and size appeals to children.

Fresh fish is available in most areas, but you can substitute frozen fish in the following recipes with little loss of nutrients. Current research shows that omega-3 fatty acid, a type of fish oil, may help prevent heart disease. The best source of fish oil is fish, and the lifetime habit of enjoying fish should begin early.

· Swordfish and Nectarine · Brochette

Colorful and tasty, this fish dish is simple to prepare and can be marinated up to twelve hours in advance. It's good with Risotto with Cheese and Vegetables (see page 167) and Baked Zucchini Parmesan (see page 135).

1 tablespoon lemon juice
2 tablespoons orange juice
$^1/_2$ tablespoon olive oil
1 teaspoon dried thyme
1 clove garlic, peeled and sliced
$^1/_4$ pound swordfish, cut into 1-by-1-by-$^1/_2$-inch
    pieces
1 medium nectarine, cut into 8 slices

1. In a medium-size, nonmetallic dish, combine lemon juice, orange juice, oil, thyme, and garlic.
2. Add fish and marinate in the refrigerator from 1 to 12 hours.

3. On 2 skewers, alternate fish and nectarines. Grill or broil for about 5 minutes, turning once or twice and basting with marinade.
4. Remove skewers before serving.

Yield: 2 skewers

·Fancy Sole·

This is elegant but simple to prepare. Brighten the plate with steamed carrots, broccoli, green beans, or purple grapes. Turbot, bass, brill, or other flat white fish can be substituted for the sole.

$1/2$ teaspoon margarine
2 tablespoons finely chopped shallots or green
   onions
1 tablespoon finely chopped carrots
2 tablespoons finely chopped fresh parsley
2 cups thinly sliced mushroom caps
$1/2$ pound sole fillets, cut into 4 pieces
$1/2$ teaspoon lemon juice
$3/4$ cup chicken broth
2 tablespoons evaporated milk
2 tablespoons oat bran

1. Grease a small saucepan with margarine. Add shallots or onions, carrots, parsley, and mushrooms.
2. Wash and thoroughly dry sole. Place, skin side down, on top of vegetables. Sprinkle with lemon juice.
3. Cover with broth. Then cover with greased piece of waxed paper or cooking parchment.
4. Bring broth to a boil. Immediately reduce heat to low and simmer for 10 minutes.

5. With a slotted spatula, remove fish and vegetables to a serving plate or individual plates.
6. To liquid, add evaporated milk and oat bran. Stir over low heat until thickened, about 3 to 4 minutes. Pour over fish or serve on the side.

Yield: 4 pieces

· Stuffed Fish Fillets ·

Children often refuse to eat fish that is prepared with the head on (like stuffed trout or even smoked whitefish) because it looks too much like a live fish. Using fish fillets avoids the problem.

3½ teaspoons vegetable oil
¼ cup chopped mushrooms
2 tablespoons finely chopped onion
2 tablespoons finely chopped celery or fennel bulb
¼ teaspoon dried thyme
½ pound fish fillet (trout, whitefish, bass, pompano)
1 teaspoon margarine, melted

1. Preheat oven to 350°. Using ½ teaspoon oil (or vegetable spray), grease a small baking dish.
2. In a small skillet, heat remaining 3 teaspoons oil. Add mushrooms, onion, and celery or fennel. Sauté over medium-low heat, stirring, until tender and water is evaporated, 3 to 5 minutes.
3. Check fish for bones. Then cut into 2 pieces.
4. Place 1 piece of fish in greased baking dish. Spread with mushroom mixture. Cover with second piece of fish.

5. Brush with margarine. Bake until fish flakes with a fork, about 10 minutes. Cut into 4 pieces.

Yield: Four 1¹/₂-inch pieces

· Poached Salmon with Peas and · Cucumbers

You can substitute any firm-fleshed fish. Also try adding diced vegetables, such as potatoes, carrots, or leeks, to step 3. It is good served with seedless red grapes or sweet plums.

1 quart (4 cups) fish or chicken broth
¹/₄ teaspoon dried tarragon, or 1 sprig fresh tarragon
¹/₂ pound center-cut salmon fillet, boned and skinned
1 cucumber, peeled, halved, seeded, and cut into ¹/₂-inch pieces
¹/₂ cup peas

SAUCE
¹/₂ cup plain low-fat yogurt
1 teaspoon Dijon mustard
¹/₂ teaspoon dried or 2 teaspoons chopped fresh tarragon

1. In a medium-size, heavy skillet, bring broth and tarragon to a boil over medium-high heat. Reduce to a low simmer.
2. Carefully place fish in simmering broth. Cover and cook for 5 minutes.

3. Remove cover. Add cucumber and peas. Cover again and cook for 7 minutes more.
4. Remove pan from heat. Cool in pan.
5. To serve, remove fish, cucumber, and peas with slotted spoon. Reserve ½ cup broth. (Freeze the rest for another use.)
6. To make sauce, in a small dish, mix ½ cup cooking broth, yogurt, mustard, and tarragon. Spoon over fish or serve on the side.

Yield: About 2 cups

· Salmon Bits ·

This is a healthy finger food for a snack or protein portion of a meal.

2 tablespoons drained, flaked, canned salmon
2 tablespoons small-curd cottage cheese

1. In a small bowl, mix salmon and cottage cheese.
2. With your hands, form teaspoonfuls of salmon mixture into little balls.

Yield: 12 bits (2 meals or 4 snacks)

· Sea Squares ·

ᘐᘐᘐᘐᘐᘐᘐᘐᘐᘐᘐᘐᘐᘐᘐᘐᘐᘐᘐᘐᘐᘐ

Here is an easy, home-made version of a favorite frozen food. The cooked fish squares freeze well and can be reheated in 5 minutes in a 450° oven or toaster oven. Serve with Creamy Tomato Dip (see page 224) made with basil.

1½ tablespoons vegetable oil
¼ cup enriched white flour
1 egg
2 tablespoons milk
¼ cup plain bread or cracker crumbs
2 tablespoons cornmeal
1 tablespoon chopped fresh parsley
1 teaspoon dried thyme
⅛ teaspoon paprika
½ pound white fish fillet (halibut, scrod, grouper, bass)

1. Preheat oven to 450°. Lightly grease a baking sheet with ½ teaspoon oil (or vegetable spray).
2. In a shallow dish, place flour. In another shallow dish, beat egg with milk. In a third shallow dish, mix crumbs, cornmeal, and seasonings.
3. In a food processor, chop fish to consistency of hamburger. Stir in 1 teaspoon oil.
4. With your hands, form squares ½ inch thick. Coat with flour, dip in egg mixture, then coat with crumb mixture. Place squares on baking sheet.
5. To cook, drizzle remaining 4 teaspoons oil over squares. Bake for 5 minutes, until golden and crunchy. Turn and cook for 5 to 10 minutes longer, until brown and crunchy. (Squares can be frozen at this point. Place on a greased sheet of freezer foil or in plastic

freezer bag, and freeze. Reheat directly from freezer for 5 minutes at 450°.)

Yield: Eight 1- to 1¹/₂-inch squares

· Fish Balls ·

Here is a great way to introduce fish to youngsters without worrying about fish bones. Some children who have trouble chewing meat love Fish Balls. Serve with Beet Sauce (see page 228) and egg twist bread (challah).

3¹/₂ medium carrots, peeled
1 tablespoon fresh parsley
¹/₄ medium onion
¹/₂ pound whitefish fillet, well boned
¹/₄ pound pike fillet, well boned
1 egg, lightly beaten
3 tablespoons ice water
Dash of salt and pepper
2 tablespoons matzo meal or finely crushed crackers
2 quarts (8 cups) chicken broth

1. In a food processor, chop ¹/₂ carrot and parsley and onion.
2. Add fish and process 3 to 4 times, until ground to the texture of fine hamburger.
3. In a medium-size bowl, mix fish mixture with egg, ice water, salt, pepper, and matzo meal or crackers. Mixture will be sticky and soft.
4. Slice remaining 3 carrots into ¹/₄-inch circles.
5. In a large pot, bring broth to a boil. Reduce to a low simmer and add carrot slices.
6. Wet your hands with cold water to prevent sticking. Form balls, about 1 inch in diameter, from fish mixture.

7. When all balls are made, drop them into simmering broth and cook for 30 minutes.
8. Remove pot from heat and allow balls to cool in broth. Remove and refrigerate for several hours or overnight.
9. To serve, place fish balls on plate, garnish with carrot slices, and a spoonful of Beet Sauce.

Yield: 16 small balls

· Tuna and Bean Smash ·

We like this served warm with a tangy green salad or with fresh fruit, such as grapes or cherries.

3½ teaspoons vegetable oil
1 cup chopped mushrooms
2 tablespoons chopped onion
½ medium tomato, chopped
1 clove garlic, peeled and minced
2¼ cups cooked white beans (or 1 19-ounce can or jar, rinsed and drained)
6½ ounces tuna, drained and flaked
1 tablespoon chopped fresh parsley
½ cup shredded Swiss cheese (preferably Gruyère)
2 tablespoons plain bread or cracker crumbs
2 teaspoons margarine

1. Preheat oven to 400°. Grease an 8-inch square baking dish with ½ teaspoon oil (or vegetable spray).
2. In a small skillet, heat remaining 3 teaspoons oil. Add mushrooms and onion, and sauté over medium heat for 2 minutes, until softened.
3. Add tomato and garlic. Continue cooking for 1 minute.

4. In a food processor or food mill, puree beans.
5. In a medium-size bowl, mix together beans, tuna, vegetables, parsley, and cheese.
6. Spread into baking dish. Sprinkle with bread or cracker crumbs. Dot with margarine.
7. Bake for 15 minutes, until crusty and lightly browned.

Yield: Six 3-by-4-inch pieces

· Tuna Provençal ·

This casserole can be made with canned or fresh tuna or fresh swordfish. The juice of the spinach and tomatoes moistens the otherwise dry fish and gives an uncommon flavor. It is good with Crispy Potato Fingers (see page 151).

3½ teaspoons olive oil
1½ cups chopped fresh spinach
2 tablespoons finely chopped onion
1 cup chopped fresh tomato or drained canned tomato
1 tablespoon finely chopped lemon, peeled and seeded
1 teaspoon garlic, peeled and finely minced
4 Provençal olives, pitted and finely chopped, or 2 large black olives, pitted and finely chopped
1 tablespoon chopped fresh basil, or 1 teaspoon dried basil
3 ounces water-packed white tuna, drained, or 4 ounces fresh tuna

1. Preheat oven to 325°. Grease a small baking dish with ½ teaspoon oil (or vegetable spray).

2. In the prepared dish, place half the spinach, half the onion, half the tomato, half the lemon, half the garlic, and half the olives. Sprinkle with half the basil and 1 teaspoon oil.
3. Leave canned tuna in large chunks or cut fresh tuna into 4 pieces. Place tuna on top of mixture in dish.
4. Cover tuna with remaining garlic, lemon, onion, and tomato. Top with remaining spinach. Sprinkle with remaining basil and scatter remaining olives decoratively on top.
5. Drizzle remaining 3 teaspoons oil over the top.
6. Cover with greased foil. Bake for about 1 hour, basting occasionally with pan juices.

Yield: About 2 cups

· Mediterranean Monkfish ·

A half pound of fish, when cooked, will yield one child's portion and one adult portion.

3½ teaspoons olive oil
½ pound monkfish fillet, cut into 4 pieces
2 tablespoons lemon juice
2 teaspoons herbes de Provence or mixed salad
  herbs
2 medium tomatoes, cut into ½-inch slices
1 garlic clove, peeled and minced
1 green onion, minced
1 tablespoon chopped fresh parsley
½ lemon, peeled and sliced into thin rounds
Toast or bread sticks

Optional: Aioli Sauce (p. 226)
  Pitted black olives

1. Preheat oven to 450°. Grease an 8-inch square baking dish with ½ teaspoon oil (or vegetable spray).
2. Wash and dry fish. Make small cuts on the skin side of each piece to avoid curling during cooking.
3. Sprinkle lemon juice and 1 teaspoon herbs over fish. Turn to coat and set aside for about 15 minutes.
4. Place half the tomato slices on the bottom of the baking dish. Cover with garlic, onion, and parsley, and then lemon slices. Place fish on top and garnish with remaining tomato slices.
5. Sprinkle remaining 3 teaspoons oil over fish and top with remaining 1 teaspoon herbs.
6. Bake for 15 minutes.
7. Remove fish to a serving plate. Remove and discard lemon slices. Spoon sauce onto fish. Arrange toast or bread sticks around fish and garnish with a spoonful of Aioli Sauce and pitted olives, if desired.

Yield: 2 cups

· Fish Hash ·

Michael really loved this unusual dish, reminiscent of traditional Niçoise peasant fare. Serve in a bowl with toasted French bread.

2 tablespoons olive oil
1 medium red potato, peeled and diced
½ pound scrod (or other flaky, white fish), cut into ½-inch pieces
1 cup canned, drained plum tomatoes
2 tablespoons chopped Niçoise olives (if unavailable, substitute your favorite olives)
3 tablespoons Perfect Pesto Sauce (p. 227) or store-bought pesto sauce

1. In a medium skillet, heat oil.
2. Add potatoes. Cook over low heat for about 5 minutes, until tender.
3. Add fish. Cook, stirring constantly, over low heat for 5 minutes.
4. Add tomatoes and olives. Cook, stirring, over low heat until thick, about 5 minutes.
5. Add pesto sauce and serve.

Yield: 1¹/₂ cups

· Breaded Bay Scallops ·

These naturally bite-size fish are ideal finger food for children.

¹/₂ cup enriched white flour
¹/₂ cup milk
¹/₄ cup oat bran
¹/₄ cup seasoned dried bread crumbs or cracker crumbs
¹/₂ teaspoon herb seasoning
¹/₂ teaspoon dried basil, if desired
Salt to taste
¹/₂ pound bay scallops, rinsed and dried
2 tablespoons olive oil

1. In a shallow dish, place flour. In another shallow dish, place milk. In a third shallow dish, mix oat bran, crumbs, and seasonings.
2. With your hands, roll scallops in flour, then in milk, then in crumb mixture.
3. In a small skillet, heat oil. Add scallops and sauté over high heat for about 3 minutes, until brown and crispy.

Yield: 1 cup

· Sautéed Rock Shrimp ·

Rock shrimp, sometimes called pearl shrimp in Chinese markets, are tender enough for young children to chew easily. Use leftovers as a filling for crêpes, omelets, Empanadas (see page 249), with rice or mixed with pasta. You can substitute bay scallops for the rock shrimp.

1 tablespoon olive oil
1/2 carrot, peeled and diced
1 tablespoon minced onion
1 clove garlic, peeled and minced
8 ounces rock shrimp
1/4 cup diced tomato
1 tablespoon chopped fresh parsley

Optional: Lemon juice

1. In a medium skillet, heat oil.
2. Add carrot, onion, and garlic. Sauté, stirring constantly, over medium-high heat for 1 minute.
3. Reduce heat to medium and add shrimp and tomato. Cook, stirring occasionally, for 2 to 3 minutes, until shrimp are done.
4. Add parsley. Increase heat and sauté, stirring constantly, for about 1 minute. Do not overcook.
5. Squeeze lemon juice over, if desired, and serve.

Yield: 1 cup

· Shrimp Salad ·

Here is a moist, colorful salad. Young children will enjoy picking out the pink, green, and yellow bites. Serve with muffins or hollow out a roll and spoon some salad inside.

$^2/_3$ cup frozen small cooked shrimp, defrosted
$^1/_3$ cup sliced ($^1/_4$ inch thick) steamed green beans
$^1/_3$ cup pineapple chunks, fresh or canned in juice
$^1/_4$ cup diced avocado
$^1/_2$ recipe Golden Dippy Sauce (p. 225)

1. In a medium-size bowl, combine shrimp, green beans, pineapple, and avocado.
2. Pour Golden Dippy Sauce over shrimp mixture and toss. Chill.

Yield: 1$^1/_2$ cups

· Sardine Spread ·

While vacationing in Nantucket, David and Michael came to love smoked bluefish pâté. This is our high-calcium midwestern version. Serve on crackers or mini-bagels.

1 can (3¾ ounces) sardines in olive oil, drained
3 tablespoons light cream cheese
2 green onions, white part only
2 tablespoons snipped fresh dill, or 2 teaspoons
   dried dill weed
1 tablespoon lemon juice

1. In a food processor, place all ingredients. Puree.
2. Refrigerate until ready to use.

Yield: About 1 cup

·SAUCES·

·Sauce Recipes·

Rich Tomato Sauce
Creamy Tomato Dip
Cucumber-Dill Sauce
Golden Dippy Sauce
Aioli Sauce
Perfect Pesto Sauce
Avocado Dip or Spread
Beet Sauce
Lemon Margarine
Quick Cream Sauce

S auces add flavor and moisture to foods. Our sauce recipes are made with healthful ingredients and use herbs, spices, vinegar, and lemon juice instead of excessive salt.

You might be surprised by your child's flavor preferences. Some children like spicy foods better than bland ones. When you make sauces yourself, you can adjust the flavors to the tastes of your family.

Serve sauces over, under, or beside a food. Vary the presentation to get different reactions from your child, or ask which ways he or she likes the sauce served. Many children enjoy sauce on the side so they can dip food into it.

· Rich Tomato Sauce ·

This is an adaptation of a recipe learned from one of the best cooks I know. She uses the sauce in a recipe for pissaladiere, *a French appetizer tart. The sauce can be frozen in ice cube trays and stored in freezer bags. Defrost as necessary. It is used in Green Fettucini with Tomato–Chick-Pea Sauce (see page 162).*

12 large, very ripe tomatoes, peeled, or 2 (28-
    ounce) cans Italian plum tomatoes, not drained
2 tablespoons olive oil
3 tablespoons chopped fresh basil, or 3 teaspoons
    dried basil
1½ tablespoons chopped fresh parsley
4 tablespoons tomato paste

1. In a food processor, finely chop tomatoes in two to three batches. (If you want a smoother sauce, puree tomatoes.)
2. In a large skillet, heat olive oil. Add tomatoes and simmer over medium-high heat until very thick, 20 to 30 minutes. Stir frequently and watch to avoid burning.

ove from heat. Stir in basil, parsley, and tomato paste.
r. Freeze if not using immediately.

Yield: 3¹/₂ cups

· Creamy Tomato Dip ·

This rich-tasting rosy dip gets its flavor from plum tomatoes, tomato sauce, and herbs.

¹/₂ cup finely chopped fresh Italian plum tomatoes
or drained canned tomatoes
2 teaspoons tomato paste
¹/₄ cup plain low-fat yogurt
1 tablespoon chopped fresh basil or mint, or ¹/₄ cup
dried basil or mint

1. In a small dish, mix all ingredients.
2. Cover and refrigerate for several hours to blend flavors.

Yield: ¹/₂ cup

· Cucumber-Dill Sauce ·

Use low-fat yogurt instead of sour cream to make this healthful, fresh-tasting cucumber-dill sauce.

$1/2$ medium cucumber, peeled, seeded, and finely
  chopped
$1/2$ cup plain low-fat yogurt
$1/2$ teaspoon dried dill, or 1 tablespoon chopped
  fresh dill weed

1. In a small bowl, mix all ingredients.
2. Cover and refrigerate for several hours to blend flavors.

Yield: $1/2$ cup

· Golden Dippy Sauce ·

This sauce is good on cold or hot steamed vegetables, with Sea Squares (see page 210), and with roasted meats or poultry. It is also an interesting dip for fruits, such as pineapple, strawberries, or pears.

2 tablespoons mayonnaise
2 tablespoons plain low-fat yogurt
1 teaspoon Dijon mustard
1 teaspoon maple syrup
$1/8$ teaspoon curry powder

1. In a small dish, mix all ingredients.
2. Serve immediately or cover and refrigerate until serving time.

Yield: 1/2 cup

· Aioli Sauce ·

ʊʊʊʊʊʊʊʊʊʊʊʊʊʊʊʊʊʊʊ

Mayonnaise can be flavored in a number of ways, by adding herbs and spices, vegetables, broths, and so on. We've included a garlicky sauce that children like and that goes nicely with several recipes in this book. If you have a jar of pimientos or leftover roasted peppers, add them for an interesting taste sensation and visual treat.

2 to 3 cloves garlic, peeled and minced
3/4 cup mayonnaise

Optional: 1 to 2 tablespoons pimientos or roasted
peppers

1. Mix garlic and mayonnaise in food processor or blender. If desired, add pimientos or peppers before processing.

Yield: About 3/4 cup

· Perfect Pesto Sauce ·

Try this pesto on pasta or roasted poultry. It also adds zest to tomato sauce and makes a great dip for raw vegetables.

    3 cups packed fresh basil leaves
    2 cloves garlic, peeled
    1/2 cup pine nuts
    3/4 cup grated Parmesan cheese
    3/4 cup olive oil

1. In a food processor, place all ingredients and puree. Refrigerate until ready to use. Use immediately or store in refrigerator or freezer.

Yield: 1 1/2 cups

· Avocado Dip or Spread ·

This is a little different from traditional guacamole. It goes well with carrot sticks, raw cauliflower, tortilla chips, bread sticks, or spread on French bread. Be sure to choose a ripe avocado.

    1 medium, ripe avocado, pitted and peeled
    2 teaspoons lemon or lime juice
    2 teaspoons ketchup

1. In a small dish, mash avocado with a fork.
2. Stir in juice and ketchup. Serve immediately or refrigerate.

Yield: 3/4 cup

· Beet Sauce ·

Vegetable and fruit purees make attractive and tasty dipping sauces for a variety of foods. This puree sauce is a steady companion to Fish Balls (see page 211) but can be served with a number of other dishes.

1⅓ cups cooked, peeled beets, fresh or canned
½ teaspoon vinegar
¼ teaspoon powdered horseradish, or 2 teaspoons
   prepared horseradish

1. In a mini-processor or blender, puree the beets with vinegar and horseradish. Store in the refrigerator in a covered container.

Yield: 1/2 cup

· Lemon Margarine ·

Lemon margarine is good over broiled or poached fish or mixed into hot, steamed vegetables. Store the margarine, covered, in the refrigerator, removing teaspoonfuls as necessary.

1 stick margarine
2 tablespoons lemon juice
1 teaspoon chopped fresh basil, thyme, oregano, parsley, or mixed herbs, or 1/4 teaspoon dried herbs

1. Combine ingredients in a blender or food processor. Blend until smooth.
2. Store in the refrigerator in a covered container.
3. Reheat as needed.

Yield: 1/2 cup

· Quick Cream Sauce ·

ʊʊʊʊʊʊʊʊʊʊʊʊʊʊʊʊʊʊʊʊʊʊʊʊʊʊʊʊʊʊʊʊʊʊʊʊʊ

This Quick Cream Sauce is one of the most versatile sauces I have found. It can be used as a base for many other sauces and soups. Many combinations of liquids can be used. Just add your choice of seasonings, vegetable purees, or diced meats and vegetables to make a thick, creamy consistency. This is a good way to increase calcium intake for children who do not like to drink milk. Stir in 2 tablespoons nonfat dry milk powder with the oats to add even more calcium.

½ cup milk
½ cup broth or water
3 tablespoons oat bran

1. In a medium saucepan, combine liquid and oat bran.
2. Cook, stirring constantly, over medium heat until thickened, 3 to 5 minutes. If sauce is not thick enough, add more oat bran.

Yield: 1 cup

·SANDWICHES·
AND PIZZA

· Sandwich and Pizza Recipes ·

Almond Butter
Banana Nut Sandwich
Nut Butter Roll
Vegetable Rolls
Bean Tortilla Roll-ups
   Crispy Bean Tacos
French Waffle
Turkey Melt
Mozzarella, Tomato, and Pea Sandwich
Egg, Tomato, and Olive Sandwich
Broccoli Burger or Veal Loaf Sandwich
Tuna and Confetti Corn Salad Sandwich
Bagels with Vegetable "Creamed" Cheese
Black Bread with "Creamed" Cheese, Salmon, Dill, and Peas
Other Combinations
Pizza Toppings—Variations on a Theme
   Vegetarian Pizza
   Meat and Vegetable Pizza
   Bean Pizza
   Tuna Pizza
Spinach Pizza
Empanadas

We've come a long way since bologna and cheese on white bread! Today's children eat sandwiches on different types of bread and rolls and crackers, on waffles, and in wonton wrappers, tortillas, and pita pockets.

Don't be surprised if a sandwich gets taken apart before it's eaten. Some children like to see what's inside.

If your child won't eat dense whole-grain bread, offer enriched breads and let cereals provide the whole grain. And try our pizza with a whole wheat crust—we've witnessed wholehearted acceptance.

·Almond Butter·

Some of the recipes in this book call for almond butter as an alternative to peanut butter. Almond butter can be found in health food and specialty shops at a rather hefty price. It is very simple to make at home in your food processor.

1 cup whole, blanched, toasted almonds
2 teaspoons nut or vegetable oil

1. In a food processor, puree almonds with oil until the mixture is spreadable and smooth.
2. Place almond butter in a covered container and store in the refrigerator.

Yield: ¹/₂ cup

·Banana Nut Sandwich·

1 tablespoon almond or peanut butter
1 slice whole-grain bread, or 2 miniature rice
 crackers
½ banana, peeled and sliced
½ teaspoon maple syrup

1. Spread almond or peanut butter on bread or crackers.
2. Arrange banana on top and drizzle with maple syrup.

Yield: 1 sandwich

· Nut Butter Roll ·

Sometimes a regular sandwich is too large for a young child's mouth. Try rolling the bread flat before making the sandwich, then cutting it into ¹/₂-inch, child-size squares, or rolling it up, as in the following recipe.

2 teaspoons peanut butter or Almond Butter
 (p. 233)
1 slice whole-grain bread, crusts removed, rolled
 thin
1 teaspoon jelly or jam
1 teaspoon finely chopped, peeled carrots
1 teaspoon chopped fresh parsley

1. Spread peanut or almond butter on bread, then spread jelly or jam
 on top.

2. Place carrots and parsley at one end of bread, fold ends in, and roll up like a blintz or egg roll. Serve, or wrap in plastic wrap and aluminum foil and take to a picnic.

Yield: 1 sandwich roll

·Vegetable Rolls·

When David was five, he created this recipe quite spontaneously. Packed with vitamins and minerals, these rolls make a refreshing lunch or snack.

1 flour tortilla, or 1 slice whole wheat bread, rolled
   thin
$1/4$ teaspoon mayonnaise
$1/2$ teaspoon grape jam
$1/8$ avocado, pitted, peeled, and very thinly sliced
1 small leaf spinach or romaine lettuce
$1/2$ carrot, peeled and shredded
2 tablespoons shredded mozzarella or cheddar
   cheese

1. Place tortilla or bread on plate. Spread with mayonnaise, then jam.
2. Along one side of tortilla or bread, layer avocado, spinach, carrot, and cheese.
3. Roll up and serve, or wrap in plastic wrap and refrigerate. For younger children, cut roll in half.

Yield: 1 roll

· Bean Tortilla Roll-ups ·

In a testing of these tortillas, David started clapping and yelling "Yeah, Mommy." When his neatly rolled tortilla arrived at the table, he took one bite, then proceeded to tear it apart and reroll it himself. The bean, tomato, and cheese combination is a nutritional bonanza, especially when served with shredded romaine lettuce salad.

1 tablespoon vegetable oil
1/4 cup finely chopped green onion
1/4 cup finely diced ripe tomato
2 cups cooked kidney or pinto beans (or 1 16-ounce can, rinsed and drained)
1/4 teaspoon ground coriander
1/8 teaspoon ground cumin
1/2 cup tomato juice or tomato sauce
Pinch of sugar
6 flour tortillas, heated according to package directions
1 cup shredded mozzarella, cheddar, or Monterey Jack cheese

1. In a medium skillet, heat oil.
2. Add onion and cook over medium heat until softened, about 2 minutes.
3. Add tomato and cook for 1 minute.
4. Add beans and cook, stirring and smashing, until mixture is pureed.
5. Stir in coriander and cumin. Gradually add tomato juice or sauce. Cook over low heat until mixture is thick, about 15 minutes. Add sugar and stir.
6. Remove mixture from heat and set aside.
7. To assemble, place a tortilla on a plate. Spread 2 tablespoons bean

mixture along one side, sprinkle with 1½ tablespoons cheese, and roll up tightly.

8. Tortillas can be eaten at room temperature or heated. To heat, preheat oven to 350°. Place tortillas in a baking dish and heat for 10 to 15 minutes.

NOTE: To freeze filled tortillas, wrap them tightly in aluminum foil. To reheat, preheat oven to 350°. Place frozen, still-wrapped tortillas in a baking dish and cook for 30 minutes.

Yield: 6 tortillas

Crispy Bean Tacos

Try these open-faced, crunchy treats with a green salad.

Same ingredients as for Bean Tortilla Roll-ups (p. 236), substituting 32 taco chips for the tortillas.

1. Preheat broiler.
2. Make bean mixture according to instructions in Bean Tortilla Roll-ups recipe.
3. Place a spoonful of bean mixture on each taco chip; top with cheese. Broil to melt cheese.

Yield: 32 taco chips

·French Waffle·

Children love the little squares on waffles. This recipe is good for breakfast, lunch, a snack, or even dessert.

1 frozen whole-grain waffle or Buckwheat-Spinach
   Waffle (p. 257)
¼ very ripe pear, peeled and sliced thinly
1 ounce Brie, cut into small slices

Optional: Sprinkle of ground nutmeg

1. Toast waffle according to package instructions.
2. Arrange pear on waffle. Top with cheese.
3. Sprinkle with nutmeg, if desired.
4. Melt cheese or serve as is, depending on your child's tastes.

Yield: 1 waffle

·Turkey Melt·

2 pieces thinly sliced oatmeal bread
2 teaspoons margarine
2 thin slices Swiss cheese
1 thin slice turkey breast

1. Spread both sides of each piece of bread with margarine.
2. In a baking pan, place 1 slice bread.

3. Place 1 slice of cheese on top, then 1 slice of turkey. Cover with second piece of bread. Top with second slice of cheese.
4. Cut sandwich into 4 triangles.
5. Bake in toaster oven or preheated 350° oven until cheese melts.

Yield: 4 triangles

· Mozzarella, Tomato, and Pea · Sandwich

Proof that a sandwich can be a lot more creative than the proverbial peanut butter and jelly!

1 slice Italian-style bread (¼ inch thick), crust removed
2 teaspoons tomato paste
Pinch of dried oregano or basil
1 tablespoon cooked peas
1 tablespoon shredded mozzarella cheese

1. Preheat broiler.
2. Spread bread with tomato paste.
3. Sprinkle with herbs and peas.
4. Sprinkle cheese on top.
5. Broil or toast in toaster oven until cheese melts.

Yield: 1 sandwich

· Egg, Tomato, and Olive · Sandwich

Try this quick-and-easy egg sandwich for breakfast.

1 slice whole-grain bread
$\frac{1}{2}$ teaspoon margarine
$\frac{1}{2}$ hard-cooked egg, chopped
$\frac{1}{4}$ cup chopped tomato
2 olives, pitted and chopped

1. Spread bread with margarine. Cut in half.
2. In a small bowl, combine egg, tomato, and olives.
3. Spread egg mixture on half the bread. Cover with second half. Cut in half or quarters.

Yield: 1 sandwich

· Broccoli Burger or Veal Loaf ·
Sandwich

Find a lovely spot for a picnic and pack up a lunch made from "leftovers."

1 small whole-grain roll
2 teaspoons tomato paste
Pinch of dried oregano
1 cooked Broccoli Burger (p. 173), or 1 slice (1½
    inches) cooked Savory Veal Loaves (p. 176)

1. Cut roll in half.
2. Spread each half with tomato paste.
3. Sprinkle each half with oregano.
4. Place meat on one half. Cover with second half. Cut in half or quarters.

Yield: 1 sandwich

· Tuna and Confetti Corn Salad · Sandwich

Youngsters manage a pita bread sandwich better if the sandwich doesn't have much filling.

1 tablespoon Confetti Corn Salad (p. 117)
1 tablespoon tuna or leftover Tuna Provençal
    (p. 213)
½ pita bread (preferably whole wheat)

1. In a small bowl, mix corn and tuna.
2. Spoon tuna mixture into pita. Serve.

Yield: 1 sandwich

· Bagels with Vegetable ·
"Creamed" Cheese

Creamed cottage cheese has less fat and more vitamins and minerals than cream cheese, which is primarily fat. You can serve the cottage cheese–vegetable mixture on any kind of bread or with whole-grain crackers for a nutritious snack. It's a great way to slip a few veggies into your youngster.

1/2 cup creamed cottage cheese
2 to 3 tablespoons chopped, cooked vegetables
    (carrots, peas, spinach, broccoli)
1 green onion, finely chopped
1 teaspoon chopped fresh chives
Pumpernickel bagels, sliced horizontally in thirds
    or quarters, or bagel chips

1. In a blender or mini-grinder, puree cottage cheese.
2. In a small bowl, mix cottage cheese with vegetables, onion, and chives.
3. Spread bagel slices with cheese mixture.

Yield: 6 to 8 slices

· Black Bread with "Creamed" · Cheese, Salmon, Dill, and Peas

This goes nicely with Roasted Beets in Orange Dressing (see page 112) for lunch or supper.

1/2 cup creamed cottage cheese
2 tablespoons flaked, cooked salmon (fresh or
  canned)
1 tablespoon cooked peas
1/2 teaspoon dried dill weed, or 1 teaspoon chopped
  fresh dill weed
4 slices thinly sliced black bread

Optional: Fresh dill sprigs

1. In a blender or mini-grinder, puree cottage cheese.
2. In a small bowl, mix pureed cottage cheese with salmon, peas, and dill.
3. Spread bread slices with cheese mixture. Cut each slice into 4 squares.
4. Garnish with fresh dill sprigs, if desired.

Yield: 16 squares

· Other Combinations ·

Minced, cooked roast beef or liver and Apple and Leek Sauté (p. 148) on toasted rye bread or English muffins

Chick-Pea Salad (p. 120) with cheese in a whole wheat pita

Lentil Salad (p. 119), tomatoes, leftover meat or fish, cheese in a pita

Avocado, cooked fish or chicken, Curried Peaches (p. 126) in a taco shell or corn tortilla

Reina's Grandma's Pretty Neat Sloppy Joes (p. 174), kidney beans, and cumin rolled into a corn tortilla

·Pizza Toppings—Variations· on a Theme

‰‰

Contrary to its reputation as "junk food," pizza is an excellent way to give your child foods from all of the basic food groups.

Vegetarian Pizza

4 ounces Whole Wheat Dough (p. 253)
1 teaspoon cornmeal
¼ cup chopped, drained tomatoes (fresh or
    canned), or 2 tablespoons tomato paste
½ teaspoon dried oregano or basil
⅔ cup shredded mozzarella cheese
1 cup assorted vegetables (thinly sliced
    mushrooms, chopped fresh spinach, cooked
    peas, broccoli, or other favorites)
2 teaspoons olive oil

1. Preheat oven to 500°. Dust a baking sheet with cornmeal.
2. On a generously floured surface, roll dough out, as thin as possible, into an 8-inch circle; or cut dough into 4 pieces and roll each out.
3. Place dough on baking sheet.
4. Spread dough with tomatoes or tomato paste, sprinkle with half the oregano or basil, then add ¼ cup cheese. Add vegetables, sprinkle with remaining oregano or basil. Top with ¼ cup cheese.

5. Drizzle oil over pizza.
6. Bake for 10 minutes.
7. Add additional 2 tablespoons cheese and continue baking for 2 to 5 minutes, until cheese is melted and crust is baked.

Yield: One 8-inch thin pizza or 4 mini-pizzas

Meat and Vegetable Pizza

Prepare as above, adding 1/4 cup cooked, chopped meat along with vegetables in step 4.

Bean Pizza

Prepare as above, adding 1/4 cup drained, cooked beans along with vegetables in step 4.

Tuna Pizza

Prepare as above, adding 1/4 cup drained, water-packed tuna along with vegetables in step 4.

·Spinach Pizza·

1 teaspoon cornmeal
1½ tablespoons olive oil
1 clove garlic, peeled and sliced
1 cup chopped, fresh spinach, well washed
4 ounces Whole Wheat Dough (p. 253)
½ cup shredded mozzarella cheese
2 tablespoons grated Parmesan cheese

1. Preheat oven to 500°. Dust a baking sheet with cornmeal.
2. In a small skillet, heat 1 tablespoon oil. Add garlic and spinach and cook over medium heat, stirring constantly, until softened, about 2 minutes. Set aside and continue, or refrigerate up to overnight.
3. On a generously floured surface, roll dough out, as thin as possible, into an 8-inch circle; or cut dough into 4 pieces and roll each out.
4. Place dough on baking sheet.
5. Spread spinach mixture over dough and top with mozzarella cheese.
6. Bake for 10 minutes. Sprinkle with Parmesan cheese. Bake for about 2 to 5 minutes longer, until crust is brown.

Yield: One 8-inch thin pizza or 4 mini-pizzas

· Empanadas ·

ᴜᴜᴜᴜᴜᴜᴜᴜᴜᴜᴜᴜᴜᴜᴜᴜᴜᴜᴜ

Another way to use Whole Wheat Dough (see page 253) is to make turnovers similar to the traditional Argentinian empanadas. Use leftovers as filling for this very simple dish.

1 to 2 tablespoons olive oil
4 ounces Whole Wheat Dough (p. 253)
½ cup filling—use Breaded Bay Scallops (p. 216),
    Reina's Grandma's Pretty Neat Sloppy Joes
    (p. 174), Mediterranean Collards (p. 142), or any
    combination of vegetables and meats
Plain, low-fat yogurt for garnish

1. Preheat oven to 500°. Grease a baking dish with ½ teaspoon oil (or vegetable spray).
2. Cut dough into 4 pieces. On a generously floured surface, roll out each piece into a 4- to 5-inch circle.
3. Place 1 to 2 tablespoons filling on each circle. Fold end over and seal by folding edges in to make an attractive crescent shape. Pinch edges together to seal.
4. Place empanadas on oiled pan, brush with oil, and bake for 10 to 15 minutes, until golden.
5. Garnish with yogurt.

Yield: 4 pieces

·BREADS·

· Bread Recipes ·

Whole Wheat Dough
Broccoli Squares
Buckwheat Waffles
   Buckwheat Crêpes
   Buckwheat-Spinach Waffles or Crêpes
Oat and Wheat Germ Pancakes
   Banana Pancakes
Orange French Toast
Herb Bran Muffins
Golden Corn Muffins
   Double Corn Muffins
   Prune Surprise Cornmeal Muffins
Pumpkin Muffins
   Apple-Raisin Muffins
   Banana-Blueberry Muffins
Tomato Sweet Bread

Bread baking and muffin making are wonderful hands-on activities for children. And there's something almost magic about waffles and pancakes that turn from runny batter into light fluffy shapes in minutes. Kids enjoy eating what they make or giving baked goods as gifts to friends and relatives.

Most of these recipes use both whole wheat and enriched white flour. Tender breads rise better with some white flour.

You'll be surprised at all the good things in our bread recipes: broccoli, spinach, bananas, squash, corn, pumpkin, raisins, prunes, and apples!

· Whole Wheat Dough ·

Give your children their own balls of dough to work with. They will enjoy the process of kneading it, punching it down, and rolling it out. I always have this dough in the freezer to use for pizzas (see pages 246–248), Empanadas (see page 249), Sweet Pizza (see page 304), Fruit Wraps (see page 288), and Apple and Cheese Pie (see page 305).

> 1 package dry yeast
> 1¹/₂ cups lukewarm water (105° to 115°)
> 3 cups enriched white flour
> ¹/₄ cup whole wheat flour
> ¹/₄ cup toasted wheat germ
> ¹/₂ teaspoon salt
> 1 tablespoon olive or vegetable oil

1. In a small bowl or measuring cup, sprinkle yeast over water. Let stand for 5 minutes.
2. In a food processor, combine the flours, wheat germ, and salt. Process to mix.
3. Add oil to yeast mixture.
4. With the machine running, add the yeast mixture. Process until the dough is smooth and elastic, about 30 to 40 seconds.

5. Lightly oil large bowl with oil. Remove dough and place in bowl, turning to coat dough with oil. Cover and let rise in a warm place until doubled in size, about 2 hours, or place in refrigerator from 2 hours to 2 days. (Bring refrigerated dough to room temperature about 2 hours before cooking.)
6. Punch down dough and roll into desired size.

NOTE: The uncooked dough can be frozen in balls of about ¼ pound each. Thaw and bring to room temperature before using.

Yield: 2 pounds (enough for 1 jelly roll, two 16-inch pizzas, eight 8-inch pizzas, or 32 mini-pizzas)

· Broccoli Squares ·

I created this bread after David stopped eating broccoli when served as a vegetable. It looks, smells, and tastes delicious. For variety, try substituting different vegetables (green beans, zucchini, carrots). It tastes best warm.

2 cups finely chopped broccoli flowerets
2 tablespoons plus 1 teaspoon vegetable oil
1½ cups whole wheat flour
½ cup enriched white flour
½ cup nonfat dry milk powder
1 tablespoon baking powder
½ teaspoon dried dill
⅛ teaspoon salt
1½ cups water
2 eggs
2 tablespoons honey
1 cup cottage cheese
2 tablespoons Parmesan cheese

Optional: 1 tablespoon sesame seeds

1. Steam broccoli until crisp-tender, 2 to 3 minutes. Reserve.
2. Preheat oven to 375°. Grease with 1 teaspoon vegetable oil (or vegetable spray) and flour an 8-inch square or 9-by-5-inch loaf pan or 16 mini-muffin cups.
3. In a large bowl, mix flours, dry milk, baking powder, dill, and salt.
4. In a large measuring cup, mix water, eggs, the remaining 2 tablespoons oil, and honey. Add to dry ingredients, stirring until just blended. Fold in cottage cheese and reserved broccoli.
5. Pour or spoon mixture into prepared pan. Sprinkle with Parmesan cheese, and sesame seeds, if desired.
6. Bake for 45 minutes for square or loaf and about 25 minutes for muffins, or until cake tester comes out clean.
7. Remove from oven, cool for 5 to 10 minutes. Remove from pan. Serve warm.

Yield: Sixteen 2-inch squares or miniature muffins or one 9-by-5-inch loaf

· Buckwheat Waffles ·

Using a waffle iron is always a treat for children. These waffles freeze well between sheets of waxed paper in a freezer bag. They can be reheated quickly in a toaster oven or microwave. When eating waffles, children can fill the little squares with small foods, such as peas or blueberries.

¼ cup buckwheat flour
¼ cup enriched white flour
1 teaspoon baking powder
⅔ cup milk
1 egg yolk plus 2 egg whites
1 tablespoon vegetable oil
1 teaspoon maple syrup
Margarine for greasing iron or pan

1. In a medium-size bowl, mix flours and baking powder.
2. In a separate medium-size bowl, mix milk, egg yolk, oil, and maple syrup.
3. In a small mixing bowl, beat egg whites until stiff.
4. Add milk mixture to flour mixture. Stir just until blended.
5. Fold egg whites into mixture.
6. Cook according to the directions for your waffle iron.

Yield: 8 waffles

Buckwheat Crêpes

With a slight variation, the thin buckwheat batter makes delicious crêpes.

1 recipe Buckwheat Waffles (p. 255), substituting 2
whole eggs for the 1 egg yolk and 2 egg whites

1. In a medium-size bowl, mix flours and baking powder.
2. In a separate medium-size bowl, mix milk, eggs, oil, and maple syrup.
3. Add milk mixture to flour mixture. Stir just until blended.
4. To cook, heat a small omelet pan. Add some margarine and heat until it bubbles.
5. Add 2 tablespoons batter. Swirl until batter covers bottom of pan. Cook until browned on bottom, about 1 minute. Turn and cook until browned, about 1 minute longer.

Yield: 8 crêpes

Buckwheat-Spinach Waffles or Crêpes

The spinach adds extra vitamins and minerals to your waffles or crêpes.

1 recipe Buckwheat Waffles (p. 255) or Buckwheat
    Crêpes (p. 256)
$1/2$ teaspoon dried thyme, basil, or oregano
$1/3$ cup drained, cooked, chopped spinach (fresh or
    frozen)

1. Prepare waffles or crêpes according to instructions, adding the dried herbs in step 1.
2. Add spinach to final mixture before cooking according to directions.

Yield: 8 waffles or crêpes

· Oat and Wheat Germ Pancakes ·

These come out light and toasty. And they're so easy, you'll make them on weekdays! In fact, the batter can be prepared the night before. Using metal cookie cutters, shape pancakes into teddy bears, stars, hearts, and so on (see note below).

$\frac{1}{2}$ cup enriched white flour
$\frac{1}{2}$ cup oat bran
$\frac{1}{2}$ cup wheat germ
2 teaspoons baking powder
1 tablespoon brown sugar, packed
$\frac{2}{3}$ cup milk
1 egg
1 tablespoon vegetable oil
1 teaspoon vanilla
Margarine for greasing pan

1. In a large bowl, mix flour, oat bran, wheat germ, baking powder, and sugar.
2. In a measuring cup, mix milk, egg, oil, and vanilla.
3. Stir milk mixture into flour mixture. Mix well. (At this point, batter can be prepared and refrigerated for up to 12 hours. Thin batter by adding milk to desired consistency.)
4. To cook, heat skillet. Melt margarine. Add 1 tablespoon batter per pancake. Cook over medium heat until brown, about 1 minute. Turn and cook until brown, about 1 minute longer. Serve with syrup, jelly, apple butter, fruit, and so on.

NOTE: Try making shapes by greasing the insides of cookie cutters. Place cookie cutters onto hot, greased skillet. Spoon some batter into cutter and cook until browned on bottom, about 1 minute. Remove cookie cutter. Turn pancake. Continue cooking until brown, about 1 minute longer.

Yield: 16 small pancakes

Banana Pancakes

It's fun (and tasty) to add ingredients to pancakes. Let your children create their own concoctions. You may be surprised at the results.

    1 recipe Oat and Wheat Germ Pancakes (p. 258)
    2 bananas, sliced or diced

1. Mix Oat and Wheat Germ Pancakes according to directions.
2. Following directions, spoon 1 tablespoon batter per pancake onto hot skillet.
3. Just before turning, add some banana pieces to pancakes.
4. Continue to cook according to directions.

Yield: 16 small pancakes

· Orange French Toast ·

Orange French Toast is delicious for breakfast—or lunch or a light supper.

1 egg
¼ cup orange juice
1 tablespoon milk
½ teaspoon vanilla
¼ teaspoon cinnamon
2 slices whole-grain bread
2 teaspoons margarine
1 tablespoon powdered sugar

1. In a medium-size bowl, beat egg.
2. Add orange juice, milk, vanilla, and cinnamon. Beat well.
3. Add bread and soak for 5 minutes, turning once.
4. In a medium-size skillet, heat margarine.
5. Sauté bread until browned, about 1 to 2 minutes. Turn and brown other side.
6. Cool slightly before serving.
7. Sprinkle with powdered sugar.

Yield: 2 slices

· Herb Bran Muffins ·

These muffins will be enjoyed by the entire family. Try spreading them with Vegetable "Creamed" Cheese (see page 243). Muffins can be frozen on a cookie sheet, then stored in a plastic freezer bag.

3/4 cup bran flakes
3/4 cup whole wheat flour
1/2 cup enriched white flour
2 teaspoons baking powder
2 tablespoons chopped fresh parsley
2 tablespoons minced fresh thyme leaves, or 1/2
  teaspoon dried thyme
2 tablespoons snipped fresh dill, or 1 teaspoon
  dried dill
1/4 teaspoon salt
1 cup milk
2 tablespoons vegetable oil
2 eggs
1 tablespoon honey

1. Preheat oven to 375°. Grease mini-muffin cups with vegetable spray.
2. In a large bowl, mix bran flakes, flours, baking powder, herbs, and salt.
3. In a medium-size bowl, mix milk, oil, eggs, and honey.
4. Add milk mixture to flour mixture. Stir just until blended.
5. Fill muffin cups three-quarters full.
6. Bake for 20 to 25 minutes, or until a cake tester comes out clean and tops are golden.

Yield: 36 mini-muffins

· Golden Corn Muffins ·

The addition of squash makes these muffins unusually moist and delicious.

1 cup enriched white flour
1 cup cornmeal
3 tablespoons sugar
1 tablespoon baking powder
1/2 teaspoon salt
1 cup milk
2 eggs
2 tablespoons margarine, melted
1 cup strained baby squash

1. Preheat oven to 425°. Grease mini-muffin cups with vegetable spray.
2. In a large bowl, mix flour, cornmeal, sugar, baking powder, and salt.
3. In a small bowl, mix milk, eggs, and margarine.
4. Stir milk mixture into flour mixture. Mix well.
5. Stir squash into mixture. Blend well.
6. Spoon mixture into muffin cups until three-quarters full. Bake for 10 to 12 minutes, or until a cake tester comes out clean.

Yield: 36 mini-muffins

Double Corn Muffins

Corn kernels add texture, fiber, and vitamins to these muffins.

1 recipe Golden Corn Muffins (p. 262)
1/2 cup frozen or canned corn kernels, drained

1. Prepare Golden Corn Muffins through step 5.
2. Add corn with squash.
3. Continue preparing according to instructions.

Yield: 36 mini-muffins

Prune Surprise Cornmeal Muffins

Pureed prunes add nutrients as well as a colorful, tasty surprise with each bite.

25 pitted prunes
2 cups water
2 teaspoons sugar
1 recipe Golden Corn Muffins (p. 262)

1. In a saucepan, combine prunes and water. Simmer until prunes are plump, about 15 minutes. Drain.
2. In a food processor, puree prunes until smooth, about 30 seconds.
3. Add sugar and mix well. Set aside.

4. Prepare Golden Corn Muffins through step 5.
5. Fill muffin cups halfway. Add ½ teaspoon prune mixture to each muffin. Add more muffin mixture to cover prunes.
6. Bake for 10 to 12 minutes.

Yield: 36 mini-muffins

· Pumpkin Muffins ·

This recipe is an excellent way to use pumpkin—one of the best sources of vitamin A.

1½ cups whole wheat flour
½ cup enriched white flour
2 teaspoons baking powder
1 teaspoon cinnamon
½ teaspoon ground nutmeg
½ teaspoon ground ginger
¼ teaspoon salt
1 cup milk
2 tablespoons vegetable oil
2 eggs
1 tablespoon vanilla
⅓ cup brown sugar, packed
1¼ cups canned mashed pumpkin (or pureed
   sweet potato)
½ cup raisins

1. Preheat oven to 375°. Grease mini-muffin cups with vegetable spray.
2. In a large bowl, mix flours, baking powder, cinnamon, nutmeg, ginger, and salt.

3. In a medium-size bowl or measuring cup, mix milk, oil, eggs, vanilla, and sugar. Add to flour mixture. Stir just until blended.
4. Stir in pumpkin and raisins.
5. Fill muffin cups three-quarters full.
6. Bake for 20 to 25 minutes, or until a cake tester comes out clean.

Yield: 36 mini-muffins

Apple-Raisin Muffins

These muffins make a great play-group treat.

Substitute 1 cup applesauce for pumpkin. Add 1 large apple, peeled, cored, and finely diced.

Banana-Blueberry Muffins

Freeze ripe bananas until you can make these muffins.

Substitute 1¼ cup mashed banana for pumpkin. Substitute blueberries for raisins.

· Tomato Sweet Bread ·

This has a lovely orange color and tastes good with cream cheese.

4 tablespoons margarine
1/2 cup sugar
1 egg plus 1 egg white
2 6-ounce cans unsalted tomato paste
2 teaspoons vanilla
3/4 cup enriched white flour
3/4 cup whole wheat flour
2 teaspoons baking powder
1/2 teaspoon baking soda
1 teaspoon cinnamon
1/2 cup milk

Optional: 1/2 cup chopped walnuts
1/4 cup raisins

1. Preheat oven to 350°. Grease a loaf pan or mini-muffin cups with vegetable spray.
2. In a food processor, place margarine, sugar, eggs, tomato paste, and vanilla. Process until smooth.
3. Add flours, baking powder and soda, and cinnamon. Process until smooth.
4. Add milk. Process to blend.
5. Add nuts and/or raisins, if desired. Mix together.
6. Spoon mixture into pan. Bake for 45 minutes for a loaf or 25 minutes for muffins.

Yield: 1 loaf or 42 mini-muffins

·SWEETS·
AND SNACKS

· Sweet and Snack Recipes ·

Chewy Energy Bars
Chocolate Tile Bars
Peanut Butter Chocolate Chip
  Cookies
Golden Clouds
Sesame Wafers
Nut Crescents
Oatmeal Rocks
Rose Petals
Fruit and Nut Balls
Apple Crunch
Broiled Bananas
Frozen Banana Coins
  Frozen Fruit
Simple Banana Frostee
Frozen Banana Pop
Frozen Chocolate Bananas
Orange Cups
Mango Icicles in the Snow
Ring Around the Mango
Pear Sherbet
Five-Minute Berry Ice Cream
Fruit Wraps

Poached Peaches or Nectarines
Jelled Orange Cream
Fruit Gelatin Surprise
Cherry Clafouti
Banana Custard
Caramel Custard
Chocolate Pudding
Bread Pudding
Brown Rice Pudding
Teeny Pear Tarts
Nut Butter Pie Crust
Sweet Potato or Pumpkin Pies
Fruit and Cheese Tartlets
Simple Whole-Wheat Pie Crust
Quick Fruit Tart
Sweet Pizza
Apple and Cheese Pie
Banana Cake
Carrot Cake
Chocolate Cupcakes
Angel Cake
Cottage Cheese Frosting
Popcorn Mix

This section has more recipes than any other one. That's because parents ask for more desserts and snacks that fit into a healthful plan for feeding children. Here are lots of ideas to try.

The recipes in this section use limited amounts of sugar and sweeteners. Although some may be less sweet than *you* like, the youngsters who tested the recipes, and who had not developed a preference for very sweet foods, were happy with them.

Some recipe books for children use brown sugar, honey, or molasses and claim that these sweeteners are more healthful than refined white sugar. In fact, sweeteners differ very little, and none has any significant nutritional value other than calories from carbohydrate. The sweeteners in our recipes were chosen because they provide specific flavors or cooking properties.

Earlier we wrote about justifiable sweets. Most of the recipes in this section include healthful ingredients such as fruits and nuts, whole-grain flour and cereal, yogurt, milk, and eggs. You don't need to feel guilty about serving these sweets and snacks to your son or daughter and their friends!

· Chewy Energy Bars ·

ᘁᘁᘁ

Serve these for a high-energy breakfast with cantaloupe and a glass of milk. For storing or travel, wrap the bars individually in plastic wrap and seal with a decorative sticker.

¹/₄ cup plus ¹/₂ teaspoon vegetable oil
1 cup shredded wheat and bran cereal (or ³/₄ cup
    shredded wheat cereal and ¹/₄ cup miller's bran)
1 cup oats (quick or regular)
1 cup dry baby cereal (preferably high protein with
    fruit or mixed, but any will work)
¹/₂ cup nonfat dry milk powder
¹/₄ cup chopped, dry roasted, unsalted peanuts
¹/₄ cup chopped unsalted walnuts
¹/₂ cup thinly sliced almonds
¹/₃ cup raisins
¹/₃ cup chopped dates
¹/₄ cup brown sugar, packed
¹/₄ cup light corn syrup
3 egg whites

1. Preheat oven to 350°. Grease a 7¹/₂-by-11¹/₂-inch or 8-inch square pan with ¹/₂ teaspoon oil (or vegetable spray).
2. In a food processor, crush shredded wheat and bran cereal. Transfer to a large bowl.
3. Add oats, baby cereal, and dry milk. Mix well.
4. Add nuts, raisins, and dates. Mix well.
5. Add sugar, corn syrup, remaining ¹/₄ cup oil, and egg whites. Mix well.
6. Press into pan. Bake for 25 minutes.
7. While still warm, cut into rectangles.

Yield: 24 rectangles

· Chocolate Tile Bars ·

These cookies are not as rich as a traditional brownie, but children like the dark, chewy consistency and milk-chocolate flavor.

1 ounce (1 square) unsweetened chocolate
2 tablespoons margarine
1 tablespoon vanilla
1/4 cup sugar
2 whole eggs plus 2 egg whites
1/2 cup dry baby rice cereal with banana
1/3 cup nonfat dry milk powder

Optional: 1/2 teaspoon powdered sugar

1. Preheat oven to 350°. Grease an 8-inch square pan with additional margarine (or vegetable spray). Sprinkle with additional white sugar to coat pan. Set aside.
2. In a medium-size heavy saucepan, melt chocolate and margarine, watching carefully. Remove from heat and cool for 5 minutes.
3. Stir in vanilla and sugar. Then add eggs, one at a time, mixing well after each addition. Add whites, mixing well.
4. Stir in cereal. Mix well.
5. Stir in powdered milk. Mix well. Beat mixture until no lumps remain.
6. Pour batter into pan. Bake for 15 minutes.
7. Allow to cool. Cut into squares. Dust with powdered sugar, if desired.

Yield: Twenty-five 1 1/2-inch squares

· Peanut Butter Chocolate Chip · Cookies

Children love "miniature" food. This is a doll-size cookie that goes great with milk or juice at snack time. Dough can keep in the freezer for up to one month.

> 1/2 cup smooth peanut butter
> 1 tablespoon margarine
> 1/4 cup maple syrup
> 1 egg
> 1 teaspoon vanilla
> 1 cup enriched white flour
> 1/2 cup oats (quick or regular)
> 2 tablespoons miniature semisweet chocolate chips

1. Preheat oven to 375°. Grease a cookie sheet with additional margarine (or vegetable spray).
2. Using an electric mixer, cream together peanut butter, margarine, and maple syrup.
3. Beat in egg and vanilla.
4. Stir in flour and oats.
5. Fold in chocolate chips.
6. Form the mixture into 1 or 2 logs, 1 inch in diameter. Wrap in waxed paper and freeze (from 1 hour to 1 month). Remove "logs" from freezer, unwrap, and slice into rounds 1/4 inch thick. Place rounds on cookie sheet.
7. Bake until golden, 12 to 15 minutes.

Yield: 40 small cookies

· Golden Clouds ·

These meringues taste very sweet but contain just a small amount of sugar. They're simple to make but require several hours in the oven. That can be done while you tend to other activities. Store for a week in airtight containers in a cool, dry place or freeze them. They are good eaten straight from the freezer. If they thaw too long, they get soggy.

4 egg whites
1/4 teaspoon cream of tartar
3 tablespoons sugar
1 teaspoon vanilla
2/3 cup toasted hazelnuts, finely ground

1. Preheat oven to 250°. Grease with margarine (or vegetable spray) and flour 2 baking sheets.
2. Using an electric mixer, beat whites until frothy; add cream of tartar and continue beating until stiff. Add sugar and beat for 30 seconds, until shiny.
3. Fold vanilla and nuts into whites.
4. Using 2 tablespoons, shape meringues into circles on the baking sheets. Press the back of one spoon into the center of the circle, making an indentation that goes almost to the bottom.
5. Bake for 1 1/2 hours, rotating pans from bottom to top shelf every 20 minutes. The meringues will brown lightly. If they begin to brown too much, reduce oven temperature to 200°. Meringues are done when they can be lifted easily with a spatula.
6. Turn off oven and leave door ajar, with meringues inside, until cool, 1 to 2 hours.

NOTE: Fill meringue cups with any combination of fruit, such as peaches and blueberries, strawberries and raspberries, bananas and berries, and so on, or brush insides with unsweetened jam and fill with yogurt. Eat immediately after filling.

Yield: Twenty 2-inch circles

·Sesame Wafers·

Try this nutritious crackerlike wafer. It appeals to young children, especially if cut into bite-size shapes with small cookie cutters.

$\frac{1}{2}$ cup whole wheat flour
$\frac{1}{2}$ cup enriched white flour
2 tablespoons honey
2 tablespoons vegetable or sesame oil
1 teaspoon vanilla
$\frac{1}{2}$ teaspoon ground cinnamon
$\frac{1}{4}$ teaspoon ground ginger
$\frac{1}{8}$ teaspoon ground nutmeg
2 tablespoons sesame seeds
$\frac{1}{4}$ to $\frac{1}{2}$ cup milk

1. Preheat oven to 400°. Grease a baking sheet with additional vegetable oil (or vegetable spray).
2. In a medium-size bowl, mix flours, honey, oil, vanilla, spices, and sesame seeds.
3. Gradually add milk while stirring until a firm dough is formed.
4. On a lightly floured surface, roll dough $\frac{1}{4}$ to $\frac{1}{8}$ inch thick.
5. Using cookie cutters, cut out shapes. Place shapes on baking sheet.
6. Bake for 10 to 12 minutes, or until lightly browned. Remove from baking sheet and allow to cool.

NOTE: As an alternative, you can press the dough into a greased, 8-inch square baking pan and bake for 20 minutes. Cut into 1-inch squares while warm, and cool.

Yield: 24 small cookies

· Nut Crescents ·

This is a healthful alternative to sweet rolls or pecan rolls. The recipe freezes well.

1 cup ricotta cheese or creamed cottage cheese
1/2 cup smooth almond or peanut butter
1 1/2 cups enriched white flour
1/2 cup whole wheat flour
1/8 teaspoon salt
1/2 cup finely chopped nuts
1/4 cup brown sugar, packed
1 teaspoon ground cinnamon

1. In a food processor, blend cheese and nut butter.
2. Add flours and salt and process for 30 seconds, or until a ball forms.
3. Divide dough into thirds. Wrap each in waxed paper and refrigerate for several hours or overnight.
4. Preheat oven to 350°.
5. In a small bowl, mix nuts, sugar, and cinnamon.
6. Spread one-third of the nut mixture onto a board.
7. Remove one package of dough from the refrigerator. Unwrap and, using a rolling pin, roll dough over the nut mixture into an 8-inch circle.

8. Cut the circle into 12 pie-shaped wedges. Starting at the wide end, roll up each wedge, then form into a crescent shape.
9. Place crescents on an ungreased baking sheet. Repeat with remaining nut mixture and dough.
10. Bake for 25 to 30 minutes. Let cool before serving.

Yield: 3 dozen crescents

· Oatmeal Rocks ·

Oats are an excellent source of fiber. Some children like the hard texture of these cookies. They are good with a glass of milk.

1½ cups uncooked oatmeal (quick or regular)
¾ cup ground, blanched almonds
⅓ cup brown sugar, packed
2 egg whites
2 tablespoons vegetable oil or melted margarine
1 tablespoon vanilla
1 teaspoon ground cinnamon
¼ cup currants or chopped dates

1. Preheat oven to 400°. Grease 1 or 2 baking sheets with additional margarine (or vegetable spray).
2. In a large bowl, combine all ingredients. With hands, form mixture into walnut-size rounds or crescent shapes. Place on prepared baking sheets.
3. Bake for 20 to 30 minutes, or until lightly browned.

Yield: 30 to 36 small cookies

· Rose Petals ·

Delicate cookies with a crisp texture, Rose Petals can be served with ice cream, yogurt, or fruit. We made them for Anne Hunt's birthday and gave them to her in a beautiful box!

1 egg white
¼ cup sugar
¼ cup enriched white flour
2 tablespoons margarine, melted
2 tablespoons finely chopped, blanched almonds

1. Preheat oven to 425°. Place baking sheet in oven to heat.
2. In a medium-size bowl, mix egg white and sugar.
3. Add flour and margarine and stir well.
4. Remove the baking sheet from the oven and grease it well, using additional unmelted margarine.
5. With a ½-teaspoon measuring spoon, place circles of batter onto pan. Flatten. (The batter will spread to 1½ inches, so space accordingly.) A standard baking sheet will hold about 12.
6. Sprinkle each circle with some nuts.
7. Bake, watching carefully, for about 5 to 8 minutes, or until edges begin to brown and center is golden.
8. While "petals" are cooking, arrange 2 to 3 wooden spoons with long handles so that they are suspended on a tray. As soon as "petals" are done, working quickly, remove them from baking sheet and turn upside down over wooden handles. (You may need to bend them gently.)
9. Repeat until all batter is used.

Yield: 24 small cookies

· Fruit and Nut Balls ·

Dried fruits and nuts are rich in fiber and many minerals. Be sure to brush teeth after this sweet treat.

½ cup pitted dates
½ cup dried black figs
½ cup roasted, skinned hazelnuts

1. In a food processor, finely grind all ingredients.
2. With hands, form mixture into ¾-inch balls. Place in mini-muffin liners or on a doily-lined plate.
3. Store, covered, in the refrigerator.

Yield: 18 balls

· Apple Crunch ·

Go for a walk on a crisp fall day. Gather some colored leaves for a table centerpiece, then have a snack of Apple Crunch. Note: This is suitable only for children over three years of age.

1 large eating apple
¼ cup walnut pieces
¼ teaspoon ground cinnamon
2 tablespoons grape juice

1. Halve and core apple. With a teaspoon, scoop out apple, cutting around the inside edge of each half, leaving a ¼-inch shell. Place the apple shells on a plate.
2. In a food processor, finely chop apple and walnuts.
3. In a medium-size bowl, combine chopped apple-walnut mixture, cinnamon, and grape juice. Mix well and spoon into reserved apple shells. Use immediately or refrigerate. Eat with a spoon.

Yield: 2 apple halves

· Broiled Bananas ·

Most children like bananas, so we've included a few recipes that are sure to be favorites. In this recipe, the banana is eaten with a spoon and the skin becomes the dish.

1 banana, unpeeled
1 tablespoon plain low-fat yogurt

1. Make a small slit in the banana skin.
2. Place unskinned banana, slit side up, on a piece of aluminum foil.
3. Broil for 5 to 10 minutes, or until softened.
4. Open skin more to expose banana. Serve with a dollop of yogurt.

Yield: 1 banana

Frozen Fruit

Frozen fruit eaten straight from the freezer makes a great snack on a hot summer day. Use any and all fruits that are in season, but do not serve to children under age three and watch older children to be sure they don't choke. Fruits like nectarines and mangoes should be peeled and sliced; place the slices in a freezer bag. Blueberries and grapes should be washed and dried and placed into separate freezer bags.

· Simple Banana Frostee ·

Once you have a freezer full of frozen bananas, here are several creative options.

1/2 frozen banana
1 tablespoon yogurt, milk, or undiluted evaporated
   milk
1 teaspoon vanilla

Optional: 1 teaspoon wheat germ or Grape-Nuts

1. Remove banana from freezer and slice.
2. In a mini-processor or blender, puree banana, yogurt or milk, and vanilla to consistency of soft ice cream.
3. Sprinkle with wheat germ or Grape-Nuts, if desired.

Yield: 1/2 cup

· Frozen Banana Coins ·

Here is an excellent way to use very ripe bananas.

1. Peel banana.
2. Freeze banana on a tray. Place frozen banana in a freezer bag or freezer container. Return to freezer until ready to use.
3. To serve, remove banana from freezer and slice into ¼-inch pieces. Serve immediately or pieces will become soggy.

Yield: ¹/₂ banana per serving

· Frozen Banana Pop ·

A quick change-of-pace breakfast on a hot summer morning.

1 banana
2 Popsicle sticks

1. Cut banana in half horizontally.
2. Carefully push one Popsicle stick into each banana half.
3. Freeze. Serve directly from freezer.

Yield: 2 servings

· Frozen Chocolate Bananas ·

In this recipe, the chocolate hardens immediately when it hits the frozen banana. Once prepared, bananas can be refrozen until ready to serve.

1 frozen banana
1 tablespoon miniature semisweet chocolate chips
    (¹/₂ ounce)
1 teaspoon margarine

1. Preheat oven to 300°.
2. Place chocolate and margarine in an ovenproof soufflé cup. Place in oven until melted, about 5 minutes.
3. Remove banana from freezer and cut into ¹/₂-inch slices.
4. Spread some chocolate onto each banana slice.
5. Serve immediately, or refreeze on plate and store in freezer bag.

Yield: 1 banana, 6 to 8 slices

· Orange Cups ·

〜〜〜〜〜〜〜〜〜〜〜〜〜〜〜〜〜〜

An easy and elegant, low-sugar, frozen dessert treat. It is good with Rose Petals (see page 277).

1 seedless navel orange
2 teaspoons plain low-fat yogurt
¼ teaspoon vanilla
1 pinch of ground cinnamon

Optional: 2 cherries, pitted and chopped, or ½
teaspoon miniature semisweet
chocolate chips or chocolate sprinkles

1. Cut orange in half. Remove inside of orange with a grapefruit knife and reserve the shells.
2. Separate orange into segments. Place orange segments in a freezer container and freeze until solid.
3. Remove from freezer and place in a mini-processor or blender. Puree until icy.
4. Add yogurt, vanilla, and cinnamon. Process until the consistency of sherbet. Put half the mixture into each orange shell.
5. If desired, top with chopped cherries, chocolate chips, or chocolate sprinkles. Serve immediately.

Yield: ½ cup, 2 servings

· Mango Icicles in the Snow ·

Slicing mangoes is a messy task. To make it easier, put the whole mango into the freezer. After an hour, the fruit is firm enough to peel and slice. The mango can also be left in the freezer longer; just thaw for 1/2 hour and it will be ready to peel and slice. Unused portions can be refrozen and thawed several times. The frozen slices are good dipped in sweetened yogurt, pureed and eaten with a spoon, or scooped into a cone.

1 ripe mango
1/2 cup plain low-fat yogurt
2 teaspoons maple syrup or brown sugar, packed

1. Place mango in freezer. Freeze 1 hour (if mango has been frozen several hours or overnight, thaw 1/2 hour).
2. Peel mango and slice.
3. Place slices on plates.
4. Mix yogurt and sweetener. Place some sauce on each slice.

Yield: 12 to 16 slices, 4 to 6 servings

· Ring Around the Mango ·

Enjoy this colorful, refreshing dessert on a summer evening.

1 frozen mango
2 tablespoons plain low-fat yogurt
4 ¼-inch honeydew rings, rind removed
¼ cup blueberries

Optional: 1 teaspoon chopped fresh mint leaves

1. Thaw mango for ½ hour. Peel and slice pulp and place it in a food processor. Puree with yogurt until the consistency of sherbet.
2. Set a honeydew ring on each plate. Scoop some mango mixture into the center. Spoon some blueberries over and serve immediately, garnished with mint leaves, if desired.

Yield: 1 cup puree, 4 servings

· Pear Sherbet ·

In fall this makes a refreshing, light homemade "ice-cream" dessert. It is perfect after a meal of Braised Veal Shanks (see page 177).

1 cup peeled, cored, and diced very ripe pears
1 teaspoon vanilla
1/8 teaspoon ground ginger
1 tablespoon milk, or 2 tablespoons plain low-fat
   yogurt
1 teaspoon nonfat dry milk powder

1. Place pear in 1-pint freezer bag or plastic container. Add 1/2 teaspoon vanilla and stir to cover all sides. Seal bag. Freeze.
2. When ready to make ice, remove pear from freezer and allow to sit at room temperature for 5 to 10 minutes to soften.
3. In a blender or mini-processor, combine pear, remaining vanilla, ginger, milk or yogurt, and dry milk. Puree until ice cream consistency.
4. Serve immediately.

Yield: 1/2 cup

· Five-Minute Berry Ice Cream ·

I am a devotee of a crank-operated ice-cream maker that works without ice or salt. The freezer bowl is stored in the freezer between uses and the ice cream is made at room temperature in the bowl. It is truly the quickest way I have found to create frozen desserts, and it is simple enough for the youngest of children to use. I've had groups of children as young as one and one-half years old taking turns turning the handle.

1 cup plain low-fat yogurt
1/2 cup fresh or frozen blueberries or strawberries
1 tablespoon vanilla

1. In a medium-size bowl, mix all ingredients.
2. Remove freezer bowl from freezer and assemble machine, or follow instructions for your ice-cream maker.
3. Pour in berry mixture and process until it sets to desired consistency, about 5 minutes. If you don't have an ice-cream machine, spoon mixture into small ice-pop molds and freeze.

Yield: 1 1/2 cups

· Fruit Wraps ·

ᴕᴕᴕᴕᴕᴕᴕᴕᴕᴕᴕᴕᴕᴕᴕᴕᴕᴕᴕᴕᴕᴕᴕᴕ

Somewhere between a tart and a cookie, these sweet treats will delight your child. And they're simple enough to let him or her assist you.

1/4 pound Whole Wheat Dough (p. 253)
2 large peaches or nectarines, cut into thin wedges
1 tablespoon sugar

1. Preheat oven to 500°. Lightly grease a baking sheet with oil (or vegetable spray).
2. Pinch off 1-inch pieces of dough. Roll each 1-inch piece into a 2-inch strip. Wrap each strip around a wedge of fruit.
3. Place on baking sheet. Sprinkle with sugar.
4. Bake for 12 to 15 minutes, until browned.

Yield: 12 to 16 pieces

· Poached Peaches ·
or Nectarines

This poaching technique can also be used with plums or pears. Try serving the fruit with a spoonful of yogurt, some chopped fresh mint, and Rose Petals (see page 277).

$^{1}/_{2}$ cup water
$^{1}/_{2}$ cup grape juice
$^{1}/_{2}$ teaspoon vanilla
2 medium-size ripe peaches or nectarines, peeled,
    pitted, and cut into $^{1}/_{2}$-inch slices
1 teaspoon apple jelly

1. In a small saucepan, bring water and juice to a boil. Reduce to a slow simmer.
2. Add vanilla and fruit slices. Simmer until fruit is tender, about 5 minutes.
3. With a slotted spoon, remove fruit to a bowl (preferably clear glass, because the dish is prettier that way).
4. Bring liquid to a boil. Add jelly and boil until slightly thickened, about 5 to 10 minutes.
5. Pour juice over fruit and chill.

Yield: 16 slices, 4 servings

· Jelled Orange Cream ·

Although I had planned to serve this for dessert, Michael and David beat me to the kitchen and ate it for breakfast. Try adding fresh or dried fruit (strawberries, nectarines, raisins) for a change.

> 1 package (1 tablespoon) unflavored gelatin
> 1 cup orange juice
> 2 cups vanilla yogurt

1. In a medium-size bowl, sprinkle gelatin over ½ cup orange juice. Let stand for 1 to 2 minutes.
2. In a small saucepan, bring remaining ½ cup orange juice to a boil. Stir into gelatin mixture. Stir until gelatin dissolves.
3. Stir yogurt into gelatin mixture.
4. Spoon mixture into 4 or 8 small drinking cups or soufflé cups. Chill for several hours, until firm.
5. Serve directly from the cup or unmold.

Yield: Four ½-cup servings or eight ¼-cup servings

· Fruit Gelatin Surprise ·

ᴗᴗᴗ

Many people think commercial, flavored gelatin is healthful. Actually, it is little more than sugar, artificial flavoring, and food coloring. This un-flavored gelatin wins nutritionists' approval because it contains real fruit and yogurt.

1/2 cup sliced strawberries
1/2 cup sliced banana
1/2 cup blueberries
1/2 cup halved grapes
3 packages (3 tablespoons) unflavored gelatin
3 cups cold red grape juice
1 1/2 cups plain low-fat yogurt

1. Lightly grease a 6-by-10-by-2 1/2-inch pan with vegetable oil (or vegetable spray).
2. In a medium-size bowl, mix fruit. Set aside.
3. In another medium-size bowl, soften gelatin in 3/4 cup cold juice for 10 minutes.
4. In a small saucepan, bring remaining 2 1/4 cups juice to a boil. Add the boiling juice to the gelatin and stir until gelatin dissolves. Stir in fruit.
5. Pour half the gelatin-fruit mixture into the pan. Chill until it begins to harden, about 30 minutes. Reserve remaining half of gelatin-fruit mixture at room temperature.
6. Spread yogurt on top. Pour remaining gelatin over, gently pushing down any yogurt that may float to the top.
7. Refrigerate until gelatin hardens, at least 4 hours, preferably overnight.

Yield: Twenty-four 1-inch squares

·Cherry Clafouti·

Several years ago I spent a week in the Loire Valley. It was cherry season, and the landlady of my boardinghouse made clafouti for us. In this version, you can substitute apricots in the classic cherry cake.

1 cup pitted sweet cherries, or 6 apricots, peeled
   and diced
1½ tablespoons flour (whole wheat or white)
Pinch of salt
¼ cup sugar
2 eggs
1 cup milk
1 tablespoon vanilla

1. Preheat oven to 375°. Grease an 8-inch pie plate with ½ teaspoon margarine.
2. Scatter fruit on bottom of pie plate.
3. Sift flour and salt into a medium-size bowl. Stir in sugar, then beat in eggs and milk.
4. Pour mixture over fruit. Pour vanilla over top.
5. Bake for 30 to 40 minutes, until set.
6. Serve cold or at room temperature.

Yield: One 8-inch cake, about 12 to 16 slices

· Banana Custard ·

Here's a great way to serve milk to a child who doesn't like drinking it from a cup. Add a tablespoon of powdered milk to increase the calcium in the custard.

4 tablespoons enriched white flour
2 tablespoons sugar
1 egg
1 tablespoon powdered milk, if desired
1²/₃ cups milk
¹/₂ teaspoon vanilla
2 very ripe bananas, mashed

Optional: Unsweetened cocoa

1. In a medium-size bowl, mix flour, sugar, and egg, and powdered milk, if desired.
2. In a medium-size saucepan, scald milk and gradually add to above mixture, stirring constantly.
3. Return mixture to saucepan and bring to a boil over medium heat, stirring constantly.
4. Reduce heat and simmer, stirring constantly, for 3 minutes.
5. Remove custard from heat. Stir in vanilla and bananas.
6. Pour custard into 4 serving dishes or plastic cups. Sprinkle with cocoa, if desired. Refrigerate for at least 2 hours.

Yield: Four ¹/₂-cup servings

· Caramel Custard ·

〰〰〰〰〰〰〰〰〰〰〰〰〰〰〰〰〰〰〰〰〰

Evaporated milk is a concentrated form of milk with twice the nutritional value of regular milk. Use evaporated skim milk if you're concerned about fat and cholesterol.

3 tablespoons sugar
1 tablespoon water
²/₃ cup evaporated milk
¹/₃ cup milk
1 teaspoon vanilla
1 egg

1. Preheat oven to 325°.
2. In a small saucepan, combine 2 tablespoons of the sugar with the water. Simmer, over medium heat, until mixture turns a light caramel color. Immediately remove from heat and spoon some caramelized sugar into the bottom of 4 small soufflé cups. (You don't have to use all of the caramel.) Fill saucepan with warm water immediately for easier cleanup.
3. In a second small saucepan, heat evaporated milk and milk to boiling. Remove from heat. Add vanilla. Set aside.
4. In a medium-size bowl, beat egg and the remaining 1 tablespoon sugar with a whisk until well blended.
5. Add heated milk to eggs. Mix well and pour into the soufflé cups.
6. Place soufflé cups in a baking pan. Place in oven. Pour boiling water into pan to halfway up the sides of the soufflé cups.
7. Bake until a knife inserted in the center comes out clean, 30 to 40 minutes.
8. Remove from oven. Run a knife around the edges. Invert onto plates. Chill for several hours. Serve cold.

Yield: Four ¹/₄-cup servings

· Chocolate Pudding ·

The boys think the best part of this recipe is licking the pan after it's cooled!

3 tablespoons unsweetened cocoa
1/4 cup sugar
1/4 cup cornstarch
1/8 teaspoon salt
3 cups milk
1 teaspoon vanilla

1. In a medium-size saucepan, mix cocoa, sugar, cornstarch, and salt.
2. Gradually add milk, stirring, until smooth.
3. Place pan over medium heat and bring to a boil, stirring constantly.
4. Reduce heat to low and simmer, stirring constantly, for 1 minute.
5. Remove pudding from heat. Stir in vanilla.
6. Pour pudding into 6 custard cups.
7. Refrigerate.

Yield: Six 1/2-cup servings

· Bread Pudding ·

This hearty pudding can be served for breakfast or dessert.

1 teaspoon margarine
1 slice whole-grain raisin bread
2 teaspoons jam
$1/2$ cup sliced strawberries, sweetened with
$1/2$ teaspoon sugar, if desired
2 eggs
$1/2$ cup milk
1 teaspoon sugar
$1/2$ teaspoon vanilla

1. Preheat oven to 350°. Grease a 2-cup ovenproof dish with $1/2$ teaspoon margarine.
2. Spread bread with remaining margarine and jam. Place bread in bottom of dish. Spoon berries over bread.
3. In a small bowl, beat eggs with milk. Add sugar and vanilla.
4. Pour egg mixture over bread.
5. Bake for 20 minutes, or until set. Cool to room temperature before serving.

Yield: 2 to 3 servings

· Brown Rice Pudding ·

Kids really love puddings. This is one Michael eats for breakfast with fresh fruit. It's a good way to use leftover rice.

2 cups milk
2 eggs
2 tablespoons sugar
1/4 teaspoon salt
1/4 teaspoon ground cinnamon
1 teaspoon vanilla
1 1/4 cups cooked brown rice
1/2 cup raisins

1. Preheat oven to 350°. Grease a 1-quart baking dish with 1/2 teaspoon margarine.
2. In a small saucepan, scald milk.
3. In a medium-size bowl, mix eggs, sugar, salt, cinnamon, and vanilla.
4. Slowly pour hot milk into egg mixture, stirring to mix well.
5. Spread rice in baking dish. Sprinkle raisins over rice.
6. Pour milk mixture over rice.
7. Place baking dish in a larger pan. Pour hot water into pan, halfway up sides of baking dish.
8. Bake for 1 to 1 1/4 hours, until a knife inserted in center comes out clean.
9. Chill in refrigerator.

Yield: 4 to 8 servings

· Teeny Pear Tarts ·

Pears and autumn go together. In summer you can substitute nectarines, plums, or cherries in these miniature tarts.

> 2 teaspoons melted margarine
> 2 slices whole-grain bread, crusts removed, rolled flat
> 1 cup peeled, cored, and diced pears
> 2 teaspoons sugar
> 1/2 teaspoon ground cinnamon
>
> *Optional:* 4 teaspoons raisins, currants, or chopped dates

1. Preheat oven to 400°. Lightly brush 4 mini-muffin cups with 1 teaspoon margarine (or vegetable spray).
2. With a round cookie cutter, cut four 2½-inch circles from the bread. Press bread circles into cups and set aside.
3. Mix pears, sugar, cinnamon, and dried fruit. Spoon into muffin cups.
4. Drizzle remaining 1 teaspoon margarine over top. Bake for 30 minutes.

Yield: 4 tarts

· Nut Butter Pie Crust ·

This pastry is made with nut butter instead of the more traditional types of shortening.

1/2 cup whole wheat flour
1/2 cup enriched white flour
2 tablespoons brown sugar, packed
1/3 cup smooth Almond Butter (p. 233) or peanut
   butter
1/2 cup ice water

1. In a food processor, mix flours, and sugar.
2. Add nut butter and process until crumbly.
3. With the machine running, pour water through the feed tube just until dough begins to hold together. Stop machine.
4. Remove dough and place on a lightly floured surface. With the heel of the hand, press dough, little by little, into a smooth mass. With a dough scraper, lift dough off surface by folding it back over itself. Repeat once more, blending with the heel of the hand. Form dough into a square and wrap in waxed paper. Refrigerate for at least 30 minutes.
5. To bake dough, preheat oven to 400°. Lightly grease an 8- or 9-inch pie pan or 24 to 30 mini-muffin cups.
6. Remove dough from refrigerator. Place on a generously floured surface and roll 1/8 inch thick. Place in prepared pan or cut circles and fit into muffin cups. Prick bottoms with a fork.
7. For a partially baked shell (one that will be baked again with filling), bake for 10 minutes. For a fully baked shell (one that will not be baked again), bake for 20 to 25 minutes, until golden. If crust begins to burn, cover with foil. Allow fully baked crust to cool before filling.

NOTE: Dough can be wrapped and frozen for up to 1 month after step 4. To use, let thaw completely in refrigerator.

Yield: One 8- or 9-inch crust or 24 to 30 miniature crusts

· Sweet Potato or Pumpkin Pies ·

These pies were a hit for Halloween and Thanksgiving. Serve with a teaspoon of yogurt or ice cream on top.

> ½ cup cooked sweet potatoes or pumpkin puree
> ½ cup evaporated milk
> 1 egg
> 2 tablespoons brown sugar, packed
> 1 tablespoon vanilla
> ¼ teaspoon ground cinnamon
> ⅛ teaspoon ground ginger
> ⅛ teaspoon ground nutmeg
> 12 partially baked, miniature Nut Butter Pie Crusts
>   (p. 299)
>
> *Optional:* ¼ cup plain low-fat yogurt or ice cream
>   for topping

1. Preheat oven to 375°.
2. In a medium-size bowl, mix sweet potato or pumpkin, evaporated milk, egg, sugar, vanilla, and spices.
3. Spoon mixture into prepared pie crusts.
4. Bake for 20 minutes. Cool before serving.
5. Top each "pie" with 1 teaspoon yogurt or ice cream, if desired.

Yield: 12 miniature pies

·Fruit and Cheese Tartlets·

These pretty little tarts are easy to make, tasty, and healthful. They are great for a play group or party.

> ¼ cup plain low-fat yogurt
> ¼ cup cottage cheese
> 1 tablespoon honey or maple syrup
> 2 tablespoons jam or jelly
> 12 fully baked miniature Nut Butter Pie Crusts
>   (p. 299)
> ¼ cup seasonal fresh fruit or frozen blueberries

1. In a blender or mini-processor, mix yogurt, cottage cheese, and honey or maple syrup.
2. In a small saucepan, heat jam or jelly over very low heat, just until spreadable.
3. Brush each baked shell with some jam or jelly. Fill with ½ tablespoon yogurt-cheese mixture. Top with fruit.
4. If desired, brush tops with more jam or jelly.
5. Refrigerate several hours or overnight, until firm.

Yield: 12 miniature pies

· Simple Whole Wheat Pie Crust ·

This makes a wonderful tart crust, even for grown-up parties.

>½ cup whole wheat flour
>½ cup enriched white flour
>3 tablespoons honey
>3 tablespoons vegetable oil
>1 teaspoon vanilla

1. Preheat oven to 400°. Grease a 9-inch tart pan with additional oil (or vegetable spray).
2. In a food processor, mix flours.
3. Add honey, oil, and vanilla. Process until mixture holds together, 10 to 20 seconds.
4. Press dough into prepared pan.
5. Bake for 10 minutes, until lightly browned. Cool on rack before filling.

Yield: One 9-inch tart crust

· Quick Fruit Tart ·

The whole family enjoyed this at a holiday party. When I'm in a hurry, I use prepared vanilla pudding.

½ cup raspberry or strawberry jelly or jam
1 recipe Simple Whole Wheat Pie Crust (p. 302),
    fully baked
1 cup prepared vanilla pudding, or 1 cup Banana
    Custard (p. 293), made without the banana
2 cups whole raspberries or strawberries

1. In a small saucepan, over very low heat, warm jelly or jam, until liquid.
2. Brush some jelly or jam over tart shell.
3. Spoon pudding into pie crust. Smooth over entire pie crust.
4. Carefully place berries into pie crust.
5. Brush more jelly or jam over berries to glaze. Serve immediately or refrigerate.

Yield: One 9-inch tart

· Sweet Pizza ·

ᘛᘚᘛᘚᘛᘚᘛᘚᘛᘚᘛᘚᘛᘚᘛᘚᘛᘚᘛᘚ

There's a little pizza restaurant at the wharf in St. Jean/Cap Ferrat, France, where the cooks make an apple tart for dessert, using pizza dough as the base. We've developed a light version of this crispy sweet that I'm sure you and your children will love. Serve it warm, with yogurt or ice cream. You can substitute ¹/₂ large pear, 1 medium peach or nectarine, or enough Italian purple plums to fill the dough.

¹/₄ pound Whole Wheat Dough (p. 253)
¹/₂ teaspoon ground cinnamon
2 teaspoons sugar
1 teaspoon cornmeal for dusting pan
1 tablespoon melted margarine
¹/₂ large Golden Delicious apple, peeled, cored,
    and sliced as thinly as possible

1. Preheat oven to 450°. Place a baking sheet in the oven to heat.
2. In a small bowl, mix cinnamon and sugar. Set aside.
3. On a generously floured surface, roll dough into 2 thin 6-inch circles or four 2¹/₂-inch circles.
4. Remove baking sheet from oven and dust with cornmeal.
5. Place dough circles onto baking sheet.
6. Working quickly, brush each circle with a little bit of margarine.
7. Sprinkle one-quarter cinnamon-sugar mixture over dough.
8. Arrange fruit decoratively on top.
9. Sprinkle remaining cinnamon-sugar mixture over fruit.
10. Drizzle remaining margarine over pizzas.
11. Bake for 10 minutes. Reduce heat to 350°. Bake for an additional 10 minutes, or until crust is baked.

Yield: Two 6-inch pizzas or four 2¹/₂-inch pizzas

· Apple and Cheese Pie ·

ഗഗഗഗഗഗഗഗഗഗഗഗഗഗഗഗഗഗഗഗഗഗഗഗഗഗഗഗഗഗഗഗ

In this dish, the sweetness of the apples and sugar contrast nicely with the slightly tart cheese. Serve this warm or at room temperature as a main course (with a green salad) or as a dessert.

1/4 pound Whole Wheat Dough (p. 253), or 1 recipe
　　Nut Butter Pie Crust (p. 299)
1/4 pound fresh goat cheese (Montrachet) or ricotta
　　cheese
1 tablespoon sugar
2 eggs, separated
1/2 cup peeled and shredded eating apple mixed
　　with 1/4 teaspoon sugar

1. Preheat oven to 400°. Use 1/2 teaspoon margarine to grease an 8-inch round pie or tart pan.
2. Roll out dough 1/4 to 1/8 inch thick. Fit into prepared pan. Prick bottom with a fork.
3. Bake crust for 8 minutes. Remove from oven and set aside.
4. With an electric mixer, whip cheese with sugar.
5. Add egg yolks, one at a time, beating well after each addition.
6. In a small bowl, beat egg whites until stiff.
7. Fold whites and apples into cheese mixture and pour into partially baked crust.
8. Bake until puffy and brown, about 20 minutes.

Yield: One 8-inch pie

·Banana Cake·

The dense texture of this cake has an Old World taste. The cake can be eaten as a snack or breakfast treat, dusted with confectioners' sugar or frosted with Cottage Cheese Frosting (see page 310).

1 cup whole wheat flour
1/2 cup enriched white flour
1/4 cup white sugar
2 teaspoons baking powder
1/4 teaspoon ground nutmeg
2 eggs
3 tablespoons vegetable oil
1 tablespoon vanilla
1/2 cup milk
1/2 cup raisins
1 cup mashed bananas (about 2 large)
1 teaspoon brown sugar, packed

1. Preheat oven to 350°. Grease with 1/2 teaspoon margarine (or vegetable spray) and flour an 8-inch round or square pan or a 9-by-5-inch loaf pan.
2. In a large bowl, mix flours, white sugar, baking powder, and nutmeg.
3. In a medium-size bowl, mix eggs, oil, vanilla, and milk. Add liquids to flour mixture, stirring just until blended.
4. Fold in raisins and bananas.
5. Pour batter into prepared pan and sprinkle with brown sugar.
6. Bake for 45 minutes to 1 hour for cake pan, 1 1/4 to 1 1/2 hours for loaf pan, until a cake tester comes out clean.

Yield: About 30 squares or eighteen 1/2-inch slices

· Carrot Cake ·

ᙧᙧᙧᙧᙧᙧᙧᙧᙧᙧᙧᙧᙧᙧᙧᙧᙧᙧᙧᙧᙧ

This nutritious snacking cake can be served plain or with Cottage Cheese Frosting (see page 310). Frosted and decorated with dried fruit, this makes a great birthday cake for one- and two-year-olds and is popular with older children too.

3/4 cup enriched white flour
3/4 cup whole wheat flour
1/2 cup oats (quick or regular)
1/2 cup brown sugar, packed
2 tablespoons white sugar
1 tablespoon baking powder
1 1/2 teaspoons ground cinnamon
1/2 teaspoon baking soda
3/4 cup orange juice
1/4 cup vegetable oil
3 eggs
1 can (8 ounces) crushed pineapple
2 cups shredded carrots (about 4 to 6 medium carrots)

Optional: 2/3 cup chopped walnuts (only for children over three)

1. Preheat oven to 350°. Grease a 9-by-12-inch pan with 1 teaspoon margarine (or vegetable spray).
2. In a large bowl, mix flours, oats, sugars, baking powder, cinnamon, and baking soda.
3. In a measuring cup, mix orange juice, oil, and eggs.
4. Pour juice mixture into flour mixture. Blend well.
5. Add pineapple and carrots, and nuts, if desired. Stir to mix.
6. Pour mixture into prepared pan. Bake for 40 to 45 minutes, until a cake tester comes out clean.

7. Cool in pan. Remove from pan and refrigerate before frosting. Refrigerate again until ready to serve.

Yield: About 24 small pieces

· Chocolate Cupcakes ·

These are good as snacks, or use Cottage Cheese Frosting (see page 310) or your favorite icing to decorate as party goodies.

3/4 cup enriched white flour
1/4 cup oat bran
1/4 cup wheat bran
1/3 cup unsweetened cocoa
1/2 cup sugar
1 teaspoon baking soda
1 teaspoon ground cinnamon
3/4 cup milk
1/4 cup vegetable oil
2 teaspoons vinegar
1 teaspoon vanilla
1 egg

1. Preheat oven to 350°. Grease 36 mini-muffin cups with vegetable spray.
2. In a food processor, mix flour, brans, cocoa, sugar, baking soda, and cinnamon.
3. In a small bowl or large measuring cup, mix milk, oil, vinegar, vanilla, and egg.
4. Pour milk mixture into flour mixture. Process until smooth.
5. Fill muffin cups halfway. Bake for 10 minutes for miniature cupcakes or 15 minutes for regular-size muffins.

Yield: 18 regular or 36 miniature cupcakes.

· Angel Cake ·

ʊʊʊʊʊʊʊʊʊʊʊʊʊʊʊʊʊʊʊʊʊ

This is a lovely light party cake topped with sliced strawberries or nectarines.

3/4 cup sugar
1/2 cup cake flour
1/2 cup wheat germ
12 egg whites at room temperature
1/2 teaspoon salt
1 1/2 teaspoons cream of tartar
1 teaspoon vanilla

1. Preheat oven to 400°.
2. In a medium-size bowl, mix sugar, flour, and wheat germ.
3. With an electric mixer, beat egg whites and salt until foamy. Add cream of tartar and beat until stiff but not dry.
4. Beat in vanilla.
5. Fold in sugar-flour mixture.
6. Spoon into an ungreased 10-inch tube pan. Bake for 30 to 35 minutes.
7. Turn pan upside down on rack to cool.

Yield: One 10-inch tube cake

·Cottage Cheese Frosting·

Let your child have fun licking the bowl from this "creamed" cheese frosting. It is perfect on carrot cake, tea breads, and Banana Cake (see page 306). Decorate the cake with fresh fruit.

1 cup cottage cheese
⅓ cup light cream cheese
1 teaspoon vanilla or other flavoring
5 tablespoons powdered sugar

1. In a blender or food processor, cream cheeses.
2. Add flavoring and sugar. Blend well.
3. Spread on cake. Refrigerate until serving.

Yield: About 1 cup

· Popcorn Mix ·

A healthful snack to have on hand for children over age three. Always watch preschoolers when they eat this mix, in case something goes down the wrong way.

2 cups plain popped popcorn
1/4 cup quartered dried apricots
1/4 cup raisins
1/4 cup peanuts

1. Mix all ingredients together.
2. Store in a tightly covered container.

Yield: 2³/4 cups

Index